TEACHER'S GUIDE 4B

Noogol

Googol

Koogol

Ooogol

Toogol

Zoogol

Consultant and author
Dr Fong Ho Kheong

Authors
Chelvi Ramakrishnan and Gan Kee Soon

UK consultants
Carole Skinner, Simon d'Angelo and Elizabeth Gibbs

OXFORD
UNIVERSITY PRESS

© 2015 Marshall Cavendish Education Pte Ltd

Published by Marshall Cavendish Education
Times Centre, 1 New Industrial Road, Singapore 536196
Customer Service Hotline: (65) 6213 9444
Email: tmesales@mceducation.com
Website: www.mceducation.com

Distributed by
Oxford University Press
Great Clarendon Street, Oxford,
OX2 6DP, United Kingdom
www.oxfordprimary.co.uk
www.oxfordowl.co.uk

First published 2015
Reprinted 2015

ISBN 978-981-01-3122-7

Printed in China

Acknowledgements
Written by Dr Fong Ho Kheong, Chelvi Ramakrishnan and Gan Kee Soon

UK consultants: Carole Skinner, Simon d'Angelo and Elizabeth Gibbs

Cover artwork by Daron Parton

The authors and publisher would like to thank all schools and individuals who helped to trial and review Inspire Maths resources.

Contents

The background to *Inspire Maths*

A letter from Dr Fong Ho Kheong

Dear Colleague,

I am both humbled and proud to see that my work has now been adapted for use in many countries. *My Pals are Here!*, the series from which *Inspire Maths* is adapted, has been translated into languages including Spanish, Indonesian, Dutch and Arabic, and the books are used by millions of children all over the world.

International surveys show that children taught with the series score higher than their peers in standardised tests, and also that it helps young children to become more confident with maths. The 2012 PISA survey again placed Singapore's children at the top of international rankings for mathematics; the country also had the highest percentage of top achievers. In the USA, it was reported in 2013 that schools in the Fayette County, West Virginia who had adopted the programme had made impressive progress in their mathematics results, including a 12 per cent improvement among third graders in one school and a 20 per cent improvement among fourth graders in another.

Why does *Inspire Maths* work? A major strength of *Inspire Maths* is its robust structure, based on best-practice principles and methods of teaching and learning mathematics, including the concrete-pictorial-abstract (CPA) and scaffolding approaches, and a systematic teaching pathway. This comprehensive pathway emphasises mastery – with continuous, active reinforcement of concepts to help children assimilate and accommodate their learning – followed by extension, challenging children to develop and practise the thinking skills that will enable them to become confident, critically aware and independent learners. The textbooks from which *Inspire Maths* is adapted have also been informed by continuous evaluation of their success in the classroom, through a process of school visits, classroom observation and programme review. Because of this, *Inspire Maths* gives you a proven framework for supporting children of all abilities to achieve success.

Inspire Maths is based on well-established constructivist ideas of learning, and the views of internationally-renowned educationalists including Jerome Bruner, Jean Piaget, Lev Vygotsky, Richard Skemp and David Ausubel. Constructivism underpins the programme's approach to learning mathematical concepts and skills through assimilation and accommodation, and their reinforcement through reflective activities such as journal writing and error correction. This perspective is also reflected in the programme's emphasis on mastery learning and building children's confidence.

More particularly, Bruner's three modes of representation are mirrored by the concrete–pictorial–abstract learning progression which is central to *Inspire Maths*. Bruner's ideas parallel Piaget's stages of development; essentially, children's understanding of mathematical concepts depends on their stage of development. Learning in the early stages is achieved through concrete representation. Then, when ready, children can move on to pictorial representations – such as the bar model – which in turn provide them with a bridge to the abstract stage, and a flexible, fully independent understanding of the abstract, symbolic language of maths. Though it cannot be used to tackle every problem, the bar model has a particularly significant role in helping children at the concrete and semi-concrete operational stage (Piaget's developmental theory) to approach and solve problems successfully.

Skemp's ideas about instrumental and relational understanding are also an important part of the pedagogy underpinning *Inspire Maths*. Skemp suggests that learning mathematics by relating ideas to each other (relational understanding) is more meaningful, and therefore more effective, than memorising facts and procedures (instrumental understanding). Building on these ideas, *Inspire Maths* is designed to develop children's lasting and profound mathematical understanding which they will continue to extend and apply.

I would like to congratulate the UK schools and teachers who have made the choice to use *Inspire Maths*. I am confident that your children will experience similar success to that seen in other countries who have adopted this approach.

Dr Fong achieved a PhD in Mathematics Education from King's College London before teaching mathematics in the National Institute of Education, Nanyang Technological University, for over 24 years. He is currently a senior Mathematics Specialist with the Regional Centre for Education in Science and Mathematics (RECSAM) in Penang, Malaysia. He has published more than 100 journal articles, research reports, and primary and secondary mathematics books, and his research work includes diagnosing children with mathematical difficulties and teaching thinking skills to solve mathematical problems.

What is *Inspire Maths?*

Inspire Maths is the UK edition of *My Pals are Here!*, the internationally renowned approach used to teach maths in Singapore, which was heavily influenced by the Cockroft report of 1982[1]. Singapore's Ministry of Education drew on leading international research on effective teaching and learning of mathematics to meet the challenge of raising primary mathematics attainment within Singapore's schools.

The approach to mathematics teaching and learning that was developed was further refined over subsequent decades and it is this approach that is central to *My Pals are Here!* Authored by Dr Fong Ho Kheong and first published in 2001, *My Pals are Here!* is used by almost 100% of State Primary schools and over 80% of Primary schools in Singapore.

Dr Fong's overarching aim in developing *My Pals are Here!* was to help all children understand and use mathematics confidently and competently, and to support non-specialist maths teachers to deliver this. The programme's success in achieving this aim is reflected in the high levels of mathematics attainment by Singapore's pupils, who are consistently ranked among the very top in international comparison studies such as PISA and TIMSS. It is also reflected in the results of schools outside Singapore that have adopted the series, for example, in the USA and South Africa.

Inspire Maths provides a highly scaffolded learning framework with problem solving at its heart. It is built on a focused, coherent and cumulative spiral curriculum that continuously builds and consolidates knowledge to reach deep understanding. The programme encourages extensive practice to develop fluency and mastery, so that every child – across all abilities – can succeed at mathematics.

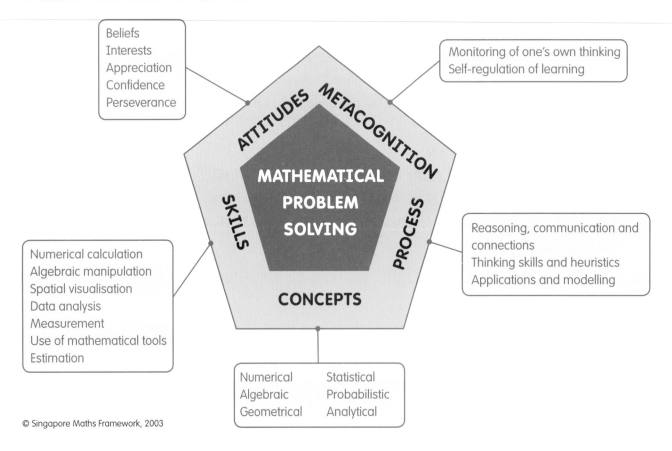

© Singapore Maths Framework, 2003

The principles that underpin *Inspire Maths*

---

1   Mathematics Counts, Dr W.H.Cockroft, 1982

The concrete-pictorial-abstract approach

Inspire Maths emphasises the development of critical thinking and problem solving skills, which help children make connections to develop deeper understanding. The powerful concrete–pictorial–abstract (CPA) approach, including the bar model method, is central to this.

Why is the CPA approach so powerful? From very early on in their school life, we expect children to use and understand numbers, which are abstract concepts. Many children struggle with this and so their first experiences of mathematics can be confusing, leaving them with no solid foundation to build on for later learning. The CPA approach helps children achieve secure number sense – that is, a sense of what numbers really represent and how to use them mathematically. This is done through a series of carefully structured representations – first using physical objects (concrete), then diagrams or pictures (pictorial), and ultimately using representations such as numerals (abstract).

In the example below from *Inspire Maths* Pupil Textbook 4A, children are exploring place value to 100 000. Using the CPA approach, they explore with counters in place value charts, then by writing numbers in place value charts, and finally through words, written symbols and calculations.

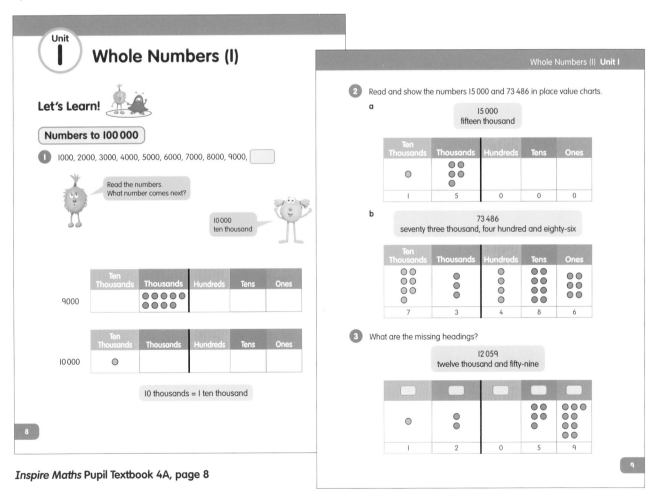

Inspire Maths **Pupil Textbook 4A, page 8**

Inspire Maths **Pupil Textbook 4A, page 9**

The bar model

The bar model is a step-by-step method that helps children to understand and extract the information within a calculation or word problem. By drawing a bar model, children translate a calculation or word problem into a picture. The approach helps children process the information given in the problem, visualise the structure, make connections and solve the problem.

The bar model is first introduced in *Inspire Maths* 2. In the following activity, children explore addition and subtraction initially with concrete apparatus before moving on to using a pictorial representation – the bar model.

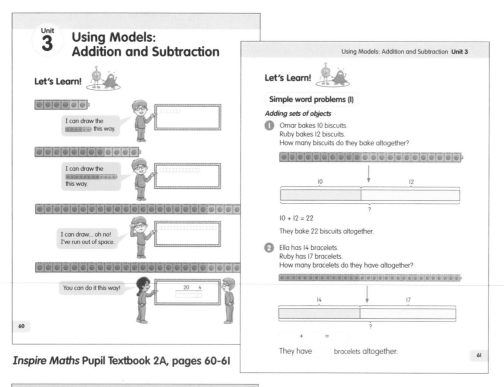

Inspire Maths Pupil Textbook 2A, pages 60-61

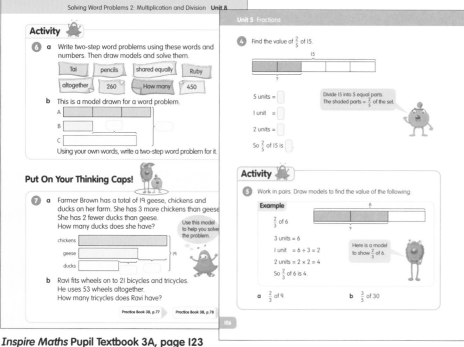

Inspire Maths Pupil Textbook 3A, page 123

Inspire Maths Pupil Textbook 4A, page 106

In *Inspire Maths* 3 and 4, bar models are applied to increasingly complex situations. Children are encouraged to draw and interpret bar models to solve a wide variety of problems. For example, they may be required to demonstrate their understanding of a bar model by writing their own question to accompany it. Alternatively, they may be asked to draw a bar model as a visual representation of fractions.

Heuristics for problem solving

Inspire Maths helps children learn to use *heuristics* to solve problems. *Heuristics* refers to the different strategies that children can adopt to solve unfamiliar or non-routine problems. These strategies include drawing the bar model, pattern-spotting, using diagrams and estimating or 'guess and check'.

In this example from *Inspire Maths* Pupil Textbook 4A, children are required to draw a table to help them make systematic guesses and then check whether these guesses fulfil all the criteria.

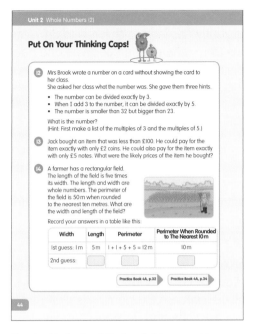

Inspire Maths **Pupil Textbook 4A, page 44**

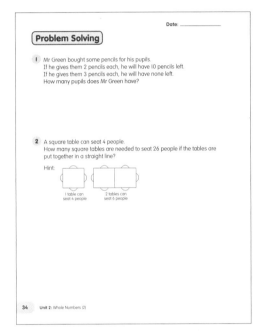

Inspire Maths **Practice Book 4A, page 34**

The *Inspire Maths* Practice Books reinforce concepts introduced in the Pupil Textbooks and provide varied, frequent practice to develop fluency. As they practise, children begin to self-select the appropriate strategy for each problem, helping them to become confident problem solvers.

Higher-order questioning

Inspire Maths is designed to stimulate thinking beyond the activities from the Pupil Textbooks. The activities should kick-start mathematically meaningful conversations through questioning, giving children opportunities to think mathematically, discover connections and be creative.

You can use written problems as a starting point for further questioning by asking open-ended questions. For example, 'Can you see a pattern? Why does it work? Does it always work?'

Modelling higher-order questioning at every opportunity will encourage children to use this strategy to explore and solve problems for themselves.

Making use of variation

Research shows that mathematical and perceptual variation deepens understanding as it constantly challenges children to develop their existing understanding by looking at questions from different perspectives and adapting to new situations. The numbers and problems in *Inspire Maths* activities have been specifically selected on this basis to challenge children as the questions progress and lead them towards mastery.

Mathematical variation

With mathematical variation, the mathematical concept, for example addition, stays the same but the variation is in the mathematics. For example, addition *without* regrouping and addition *with* regrouping. The variation challenges children to use their mathematical skills flexibly to suit the situation, deepening understanding.

Perceptual variation

With perceptual variation, the mathematical concept is the same throughout the sequence of questions but is presented in different ways. In this example from *Inspire Maths* Pupil Textbook 4B, perceptual variation is provided by the use of diagrams and number lines alongside fractions and decimals, leading to a deeper understanding of tenths.

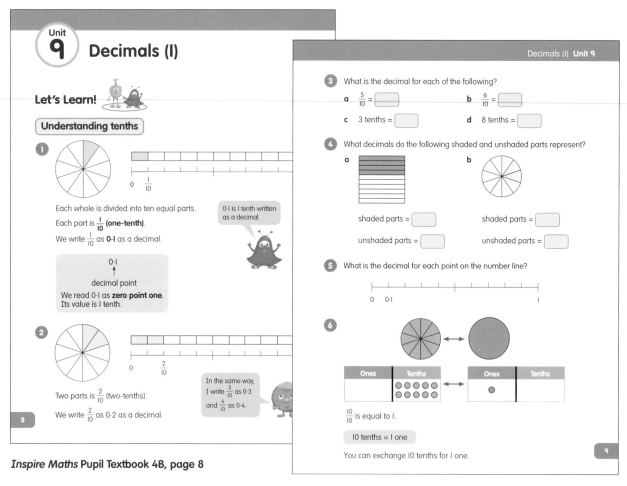

Inspire Maths Pupil Textbook 4B, page 8

Inspire Maths Pupil Textbook 4B, page 9

The *Inspire Maths* teaching pathway

Inspire Maths is a programme that teaches to mastery. It is built on a cumulative spiral curriculum, focusing on core topics to build deep understanding. The *Inspire Maths* teaching pathway scaffolds in-depth learning of key mathematical concepts through the development of problem-solving and critical thinking skills, and extensive opportunities for practice.

Pupil Textbooks to scaffold new learning

Inspire Maths Pupil Textbooks present new learning clearly and consistently, providing a highly scaffolded framework to support all children. Mathematical concepts are presented visually, with specific and structured activities, to build firm foundations. There are two Pupil Textbooks for each level.

Let's Learn! to build firm foundations

Carefully scaffolded learning through *Let's Learn!* activities in the *Inspire Maths* Pupil Textbooks promotes deep mathematical understanding through:

- clearly presented pages to illustrate how the CPA approach can be used to build firm foundations

- careful questioning to support the use of concrete apparatus

- opportunities for higher-order questioning (see page ix) to help children become confident and competent problem solvers

- opportunities to assess each child's understanding and prior knowledge through observing their use of concrete apparatus and how they approach the activity

- use of mathematical talk to explore and develop reasoning skills.

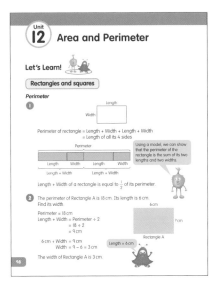

Inspire Maths Pupil Textbook 4B, page 98

Guided practice to develop deep understanding

After a concept has been introduced in *Let's Learn!*, guided practice develops the deep understanding required for mastery. Support and guide children as they work collaboratively in pairs or small groups through the guided practice activities indicated by empty coloured boxes in the Pupil Textbook.

Frequent opportunities for guided practice:

- help children develop deep understanding

- develop mathematical language and reasoning through collaborative work

- provide further opportunities to check children's understanding by observing their use of concrete apparatus and listening to their discussions

- help you to provide appropriate intervention – guiding those who need extra support and challenging those who are ready for the next step.

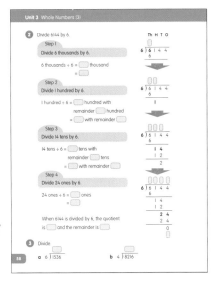

Inspire Maths Pupil Textbook 4A, page 58

Let's Explore! and Games to investigate and apply learning

Engaging games and investigative *Let's Explore!* activities in the *Inspire Maths* Pupil Textbooks encourage children to apply concepts they have been learning and provide an opportunity to assess their reasoning skills by observing how they approach the tasks.

Children work collaboratively in small groups or pairs:

- games reinforce skills, concepts and problem solving strategies leading to mastery

- *Let's Explore!* activities encourage children to investigate connections through mathematical reasoning

- meaningful discussion and conversation develop mathematical language.

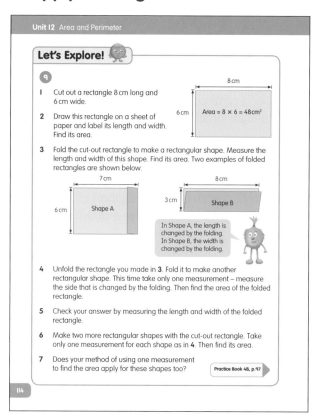

Inspire Maths Pupil Textbook 4B, page 114

Maths Journal to reflect

The *Maths Journal* is where each child records their mathematical thinking and reflects on their learning. The typical Maths Journal would be a child's own exercise book or notebook – something that the child 'owns', can share with you, with parents or carers, and that builds up over time.

Children reflect on their learning through their Maths Journal:

- giving both the child and you a valuable assessment tool, showing progress over time

- providing opportunities for children to discuss their thinking with each other, parents or carers, and with you, helping to establish next steps and giving a sense of pride in their achievements.

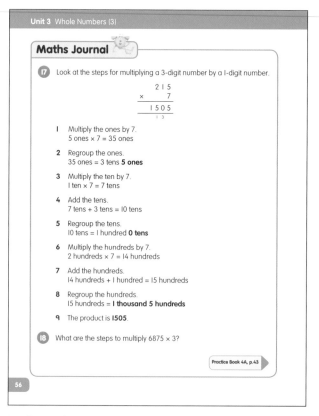

Inspire Maths Pupil Textbook 4A, page 56

Put on Your Thinking Caps! to challenge

Each unit concludes with a *Put on Your Thinking Caps!* activity in the Pupil Textbook which challenges children to solve non-routine problems.

Challenging activities:

- ask children to draw on prior knowledge as well as newly learned concepts

- ask children to use problem solving strategies and critical thinking skills, for example sequencing or comparing

- provide valuable opportunities to assess whether children have developed a deep understanding of a concept by listening to their explanations of their mathematical thinking and looking at how they model the problem, for example using concrete apparatus and pictorial representations.

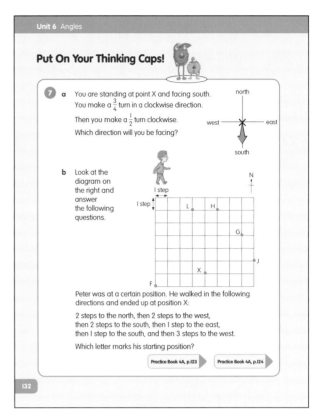

Inspire Maths Pupil Textbook 4A, page 132

Home Maths to encourage mathematical conversations

Home maths activities in the Pupil Textbooks are engaging, hands-on suggestions that parents and carers can use with children to explore maths further outside the classroom, for example through finding shapes in pictures and around the house.

Engaging home activities:

- help you to involve parents and carers in their child's mathematical learning

- help children to see maths in the world around them.

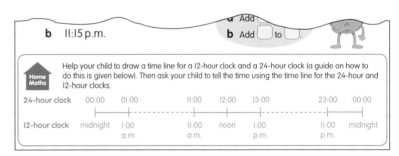

Inspire Maths Pupil Textbook 4B, page 88

Practice Books to develop fluency and consolidate

Inspire Maths Practice Books provide carefully structured questions to reinforce concepts introduced in the Pupil Textbooks and to provide varied, frequent practice. A wealth of activities develop fluency, build mathematical confidence and lead towards mastery. The Practice Books are also a valuable record of individual progress. There are four Practice Books for *Inspire Maths* 1-3 and two Practice Books for *Inspire Maths* 4-6.

Each Practice Book includes:

- **Challenging Practice** and **Problem Solving** activities to develop children's critical thinking skills

- **Reviews** after every two or three units, to reinforce learning

- **Revisions** that draw from a range of preceding topics, concepts and strands, for more complete consolidation.

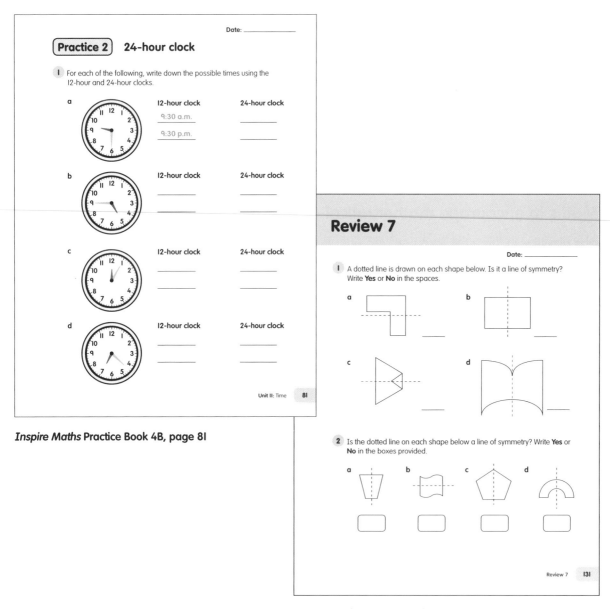

Inspire Maths Practice Book 4B, page 81

Inspire Maths Practice Book 4B, page 131

Assessment Books to create a record of progress

Inspire Maths provides comprehensive Assessment Books with regular summative assessments to create a record of progress for each child, as well as giving children opportunities to reflect on their own learning. The wraparound assessment provided through the *Inspire Maths* teaching pathway in combination with the *Inspire Maths* Assessment Books enables rapid, appropriate intervention as soon as a child needs it, before they fall behind and when they are ready to be challenged. Topics and concepts are frequently revisited in the assessments, helping to build mastery.

There is one Assessment Book for each level, providing complete coverage of the key concepts across a year. Each assessment is divided into sections so you can easily break them down into appropriate chunks to suit your class. For the early levels, you may choose to assess in small groups, reading out the questions and scribing answers. Encourage children to use concrete apparatus when they need support to help them work through the questions.

There are three types of assessment within each Assessment Book:

1. **Main assessments:** The main assessments cover the key learning objectives from the preceding two or three units of the Pupil Textbooks. Through the main assessments, children are given opportunities to apply their learning in a variety of different contexts, helping you to quickly identify which children are ready to move on and which need further support. Children may self-mark to reflect on their progress.

2. **Check-ups:** There are four check-ups for each level which revisit the previous units, drawing on prior knowledge to encourage children to make connections and apply their learning to solve problems. These assessments give you valuable opportunities to check children's understanding through observing how they approach questions, use and interpret mathematical language and use heuristics.

3. **Challenging Problems:** These assessments make use of non-routine and unfamiliar questions to see how children use their repertoire of strategies to tackle more challenging problems. Use this as an opportunity to assess children's mathematical thinking, reasoning and problem solving skills by looking at their methods and how they approach the problem. They are particularly suitable for extension and assessing a child's level of mastery.

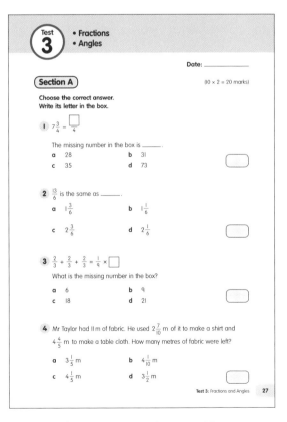

Inspire Maths Assessment Book 4, page 27

Using the Teacher's Guide

There are two *Inspire Maths* Teacher's Guides for each level, one per Pupil Textbook. Each Teacher's Guide contains:

- information on how to get started
- long-term planning support
- medium-term planning support
- suggested teaching sequence for each pupil textbook page
- answers
- photocopiable activities.

Key thinking skills and problem solving strategies to look for and encourage are clearly highlighted, helping you to make meaningful assessments of children's understanding.

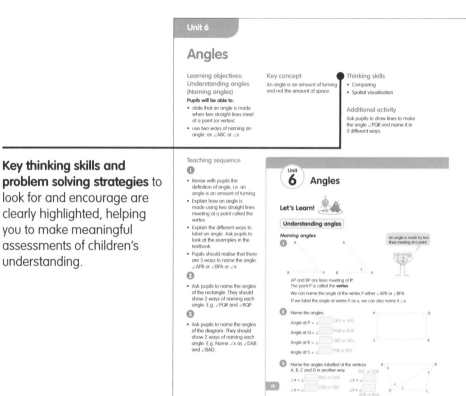

Inspire Maths Teacher's Guide 4A, pages 186-187

Ideas for **further practice activities** to develop fluency are outlined in every unit.

Opportunities are flagged for children to work independently in their **Maths Journal**, to record and reflect on their learning, leading towards mastery.

Links to the Practice Books provide opportunities for **independent work** when children are ready, to develop fluency and lead towards mastery.

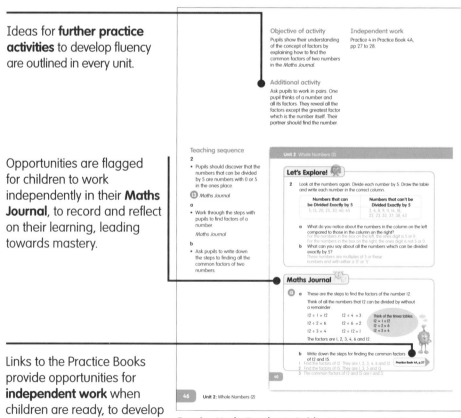

Inspire Maths Teacher's Guide 4A, pages 46-47

Key concepts clearly outline the important ideas children will be introduced to within each unit.

Equipment needed for each Pupil Textbook page is listed to help you prepare for the activities.

Learning objectives clearly signal the aims of the unit, which are designed to help children develop their understanding of the unit's key concepts. Children are introduced to the learning objectives in the Pupil Textbook. The Practice Book provides opportunities to practise and consolidate for mastery.

The **teaching sequence** provides clear step-by-step guidance towards meeting the learning objectives. It highlights problem solving strategies to focus on and support for meaningful mathematical conversation and making the best use of concrete apparatus.

Learning objectives:
Understanding angles
(Measuring angles)
Pupils will be able to:
- state that an angle is measured in degrees (°)
- measure angles (up to 180°) with a protractor
- use the outer scale and the inner scale of the protractor discriminately
- compare angles and state whether an angle is greater or smaller than a right angle

- estimate the size of an angle
- estimate if an angle is a right angle, smaller than a right angle or greater than a right angle

Key concept
Angles are named as ∠ABC or ∠a.

What you will need
- Paper for folding right angles
- Protractor (see Photocopy master 3 on page 261)

Additional activity
Ask pupils to work in pairs. Pupil A draws an angle and Pupil B names the angle. Pupils A and B swap roles.

Teaching sequence

1
- Revise the Year 3 topic about how to use a right angle made from a piece of folded paper to measure or estimate if an angle is a right angle.
- Introduce the unit of measure: degrees (°)
- Show pupils a protractor and tell them that angles are measured with a protractor.
- Show pupils the features of a protractor. Show pupils the base line and centre of the protractor. Explain that there are two scales.
- Demonstrate the right angle 90° with the protractor and the folded paper. Ask pupils to make a right angle with a piece of folded paper and check using a protractor if the angle is a right angle, greater than a right angle or smaller than a right angle.
- Demonstrate the steps to measure an angle given in the textbook.

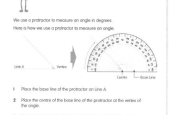

Measuring angles

Angles **Unit 6**

We measure angles in degrees. 90 degrees is written as 90°.

We use a protractor to measure an angle in degrees.
Here is how we use a protractor to measure an angle.

Line A   Vertex

Centre   Base Line

1 Place the base line of the protractor on Line A.

2 Place the centre of the base line of the protractor at the vertex of the angle.

3 Read the outer scale. The line passes through the 45° mark. The angle is 45°.

We read the outer scale because the zero on the outer scale lies on Line A.

Learning objectives:
Multiples
Pupils will be able to:
- state that a multiple of a whole number is a product of this whole number and another whole number
- determine if a whole number is a multiple of another 1-digit whole number by division
- list the first 12 multiples of a given 1-digit whole number
- identify the common multiples of two or three 1-digit whole numbers

- relate the concepts of 'factors' and 'multiples'

Key concepts
- Multiples of a 1-digit whole number are found by multiplying the whole number by any other whole number.
- The concept of factors and multiples are related: 2 is a factor of 8 and 8 is a multiple of 2.

Additional activity
Encourage pupils to recite the multiplication tables of 4 and 9. Then ask them to write down the first 10 multiples of 4 and 9.

Teaching sequence

1
- Introduce the word 'multiple' by relating it to the multiplication table.
- Ask pupils to recite the 3 times table. The products obtained from the 3 times table are multiples of 3.

2
- Demonstrate and explain to pupils the strategy of how to determine whether a number is a multiple of another number. Use the divisibility rule in your demonstration.
- Explain that a number is a multiple if it divides by the original number exactly.

3
- Ask pupils to work in pairs to practise the strategy in **2** to find out if a number is a multiple of another number.

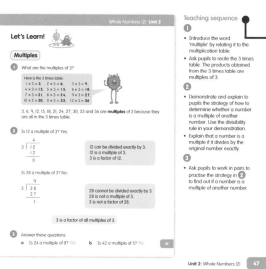

Let's Learn!

Whole Numbers (2) **Unit 2**

Multiples

1 What are the multiples of 3?

Here is the 3 times table:
1 × 3 = 3,   2 × 3 = 6,   3 × 3 = 9,
4 × 3 = 12, 5 × 3 = 15, 6 × 3 = 18,
7 × 3 = 21, 8 × 3 = 24, 9 × 3 = 27,
10 × 3 = 30, 11 × 3 = 33, 12 × 3 = 36

3, 6, 9, 12, 15, 18, 21, 24, 27, 30, 33 and 36 are **multiples** of 3 because they are all in the 3 times table.

2 Is 12 a multiple of 3? Yes.

    4
3) 12
  12
   0

12 can be divided exactly by 3.
12 is a multiple of 3.
3 is a factor of 12.

Is 28 a multiple of 3? No.

    9
3) 28
  27
   1

28 cannot be divided exactly by 3.
28 is not a multiple of 3.
3 is not a factor of 28.

3 is a factor of all multiples of 3.

3 Answer these questions.
a Is 24 a multiple of 8? Yes   b Is 42 a multiple of 5? No

Long-term planning

Unit title	Key concepts
1 Whole Numbers (1)	
Numbers to 100 000	• Place value of ten thousands, thousands, hundreds, tens and ones and counting numbers up to 100 000
Comparing numbers with 100 000	• Numbers up to 100 000 are compared and arranged in ascending or descending order
2 Whole Numbers (2)	
Rounding numbers to the nearest ten	• The number line is used as a visual aid to help pupils round numbers
Rounding numbers to the nearest hundred	
Estimation	• Estimation is based on rounding numbers and it provides a tool for checking answers
Factors	• Factors are whole numbers. When a given number is divided by its factor, it does not leave any remainder • The smallest factor of a number is 1 and the greatest factor is the number itself
Multiples	• Multiples of a 1-digit whole number are found by multiplying the whole number by any other whole number • The concept of factors and multiples are related: 2 is a factor of 8 and 8 is a multiple of 2
Practice Book - Review 1	
Assessment Book – Test 1	
3 Whole Numbers (3)	
Multiplication by a 1-digit number	• Using a formal algorithm to multiply numbers up to 4 digits by a 1-digit whole number • Using regrouping in multiplication
Multiplication by a 2-digit number	• Using a formal algorithm to multiply numbers up to 3 digits by a 2-digit whole number • Using regrouping in multiplication
Division by a 1-digit number	• Using a formal algorithm to divide a number up to 4 digits by a 1-digit whole number • Regrouping is involved in division
Word problems	• Applying concepts in the 4 operations to solve word problems up to 3 steps involving whole numbers and the 4 operations (some word problems are solved with the help of models)

Unit title	Key concepts
4 Tables and Line Graphs	
Presenting and interpreting data in a table	• Data involving two variables is presented in a table
More tables	• A variable may be sub-classified into two or more sub-variables (e.g. 'Number of children' can be further classified into 'Number of boys' and 'Number of girls')
Line graphs	
Practice Book – Review 2	
Assessment Book – Test 2, Challenging Problems I, Check-up I	
5 Fractions	
Mixed numbers	• A mixed number is made up of a whole number and a proper fraction • A proper fraction is a part of a whole • A proper fraction is a number between 0 and I
Improper fractions	• In an improper fraction, the numerator is equal to or greater than the denominator • An improper fraction is a number equal to or greater than I • Improper fractions are extensions of proper fractions
Conversion of fractions	• A mixed number and an improper fraction can represent the same number
Adding and subtracting fractions	• Two fractions are related when the denominator of one fraction is a multiple of the denominator of the other fraction • Two or more related fractions can be converted to equivalent fractions with denominators equal to that of the fraction with the greatest denominator
Fractions of a set	• A fraction is part of a set
Word problems	• Applying the concepts of a fraction as part of a whole and part of a set
6 Angles	
Understanding angles (Naming angles)	• An angle is an amount of turning and not the amount of space
Understanding angles (Measuring angles)	• Angles are named as $\angle ABC$ or $\angle a$
Drawing angles to 180°	• Drawing angles up to 180°
Turns and right angles	• A right angle (a quarter turn) is 90°, 2 right angles (a half turn) is 180°, 3 right angles (a three-quarter turn) is 270° and 4 right angles (a complete turn) is 360°
8-point compass	• The directions: north (N), south (S), east (E), west (W), north-east (NE), north-west (NW), south-east (SE), south-west (SW)
Practice Book – Review 3	
Assessment Book – Test 3	

Unit title	Key concepts
7 Perpendicular and Parallel Lines	
Drawing perpendicular lines	• Perpendicular lines meet or intersect at right angles
Drawing parallel lines	• Parallel lines never meet • The perpendicular distance between a pair of parallel lines is equal at every point on the lines
Horizontal and vertical lines	• A horizontal line is a line on level ground or parallel to the level ground • A vertical line is a line perpendicular to the level ground
8 Squares and Rectangles	
Squares and rectangles	• A square is a four-sided shape in which all the sides are equal and all the angles are right angles • A rectangle is a four-sided shape in which the opposite sides are equal and all the angles are right angles
More on squares and rectangles	• Properties of squares (all the sides are equal and each angle = 90°) and rectangles (opposite sides are equal and each angle = 90°)
Practice Book – Review 4	
Practice Book – Revision I	
Assessment Book – Test 4, Challenging Problems 2, Check-up 2	
9 Decimals (I)	
Understanding tenths	• The first decimal place represents tenths • 10 tenths = 1 one
Understanding hundredths	• The second decimal place represents hundredths • 10 hundredths = 1 tenth
Understanding thousandths	• The third decimal place represents thousandths • 10 thousandths = 1 hundredth
Comparing decimals	• Decimals form part of the base-ten system of numeration
Rounding decimals	• Between two consecutive whole numbers, there are 10 tenths • Between two consecutive tenths, there are 10 hundredths • Between two consecutive hundredths, there are 10 thousandths
Fractions and decimals	• Decimals up to 3 places are fractions with denominators 10, 100, 1000

Unit title	Key concepts
10 Decimals (2)	
Addition	Addition of decimals can be interpreted as: • combining two or more quantities into one • the enlargement of a quantity, i.e. increasing the amount in the quantity • comparison of a quantity with another, i.e. one quantity has a certain amount more than the other
Subtraction	Subtraction of decimals can be interpreted as: • taking away part of a quantity • finding the missing part of a quantity given the whole and the other part • comparison, i.e. the difference between two quantities • complementary addition, i.e. how much must be added to a quantity to give another
Word problems	• Applying the concepts of addition and subtraction of decimals to solving word problems
Multiplication	Multiplication of a decimal by a whole number can be interpreted as: • repeated addition of the decimal • comparison of one quantity with another, i.e. one quantity is n times as much as the other
Division	Division of a decimal by a whole number can be interpreted as: • sharing equally, i.e. dividing the decimal into a number of equal groups. The number of groups is determined by the divisor • grouping equally, i.e. dividing the set into groups of equal size. The size of each group is determined by the divisor
Estimation of decimals	• Applying rounding concepts and mental calculation strategies
Word problems	• Applying the concepts of multiplication and division of a decimal by a whole number to solving word problems
Practice Book – Review 5	
11 Time	
Seconds	• A second is a unit of measurement of time • 60 seconds = 1 minute
24-hour clock	• Time can be expressed using the 12-hour or the 24-hour clock notation • Duration can be measured in hours and minutes
Assessment Book – Test 5, Challenging Problems 3, Check-up 3	

Unit title	Key concepts
12 Area and Perimeter	
Rectangles and squares	• The perimeter of a plane closed figure is the distance around the figure. For a rectangle, the perimeter is 2 × (Length + Width) and for a square, it is 4 × Length of side • The area of a plane closed figure is the amount of surface inside the figure. For a rectangle, the area is Length × Width and for a square, it is Side × Side
Composite shapes	• The perimeter of a composite shape is the total distance around it • The area of a composite shape is the sum of the areas of all the individual rectangles and squares that make up the composite shape • Area of a rectangle = Length × Width and Area of a square = Side × Side • Opposite sides of a rectangle are equal • The four sides of a square are equal
Solving word problems	• Applying the concepts of area and perimeter of squares and rectangles to solving word problems
Practice Book – Review 6	
13 Symmetry	
Identifying symmetrical shapes	• A symmetrical shape has a line of symmetry which divides the shape into two equal parts • When folded along the line of symmetry, the two parts fit exactly
Identifying lines of symmetry	• A line of symmetry divides the shape into two equal parts so that the two parts fit exactly when the shape is folded along this line
Making symmetrical shapes and patterns	• A shape is symmetrical along a line if the line divides the shape into two equal parts and the parts fit exactly when the shape is folded along this line
14 Tessellations	
Identifying tessellations	• A shape can be tessellated if any number of them can be fitted together to cover a surface without any gaps or overlapping. If necessary, the shape can be rotated, but not flipped over
More tessellations	• A tessellating shape can cover a surface without any gaps • Some tessellating shapes can cover a surface in more than one way • A tessellating shape can be created from another
Practice Book – Review 7	
Practice Book – Revision 2	
Assessment Book – Test 6, Challenging Problems 4, Check-up 4	

Medium-term plan

Week	Learning Objectives	Thinking Skills	Resources
1	**(1) Understanding tenths** Pupils will be able to: • read and write tenths as decimals (1 decimal place) • represent and interpret tenths in region, number line and place value models • recognise that 10 tenths = 1 one • write a fraction with denominator 10 as a decimal	• Translating decimal representation to models and vice versa • Translating fraction statements and verbal statements to decimals • Relating number line representation to decimals • Applying place value concepts	• Pupil Textbook 4B, pp 8 to 13 • Practice Book 4B, pp 7 to 10 • Teacher's Guide 4B, pp 6 to 11
1	**(2) Understanding hundredths** Pupils will be able to: • read and write hundredths as decimals (2 decimal places) • represent and interpret hundredths in region, number line and place value models • recognise that 10 hundredths = 1 tenth • write a fraction with denominator 100 as a decimal	• Translating decimal representation to models and vice versa • Translating fraction statements and verbal statements to decimals • Relating number line representation to decimals • Applying place value concepts	• Pupil Textbook 4B, pp 14 to 20 • Practice Book 4B, pp 11 to 14 • Teacher's Guide 4B, pp 12 to 18

Unit 9: Decimals (I)

Week		Learning Objectives	Thinking Skills	Resources
1–2	**(3) Understanding thousandths**	Pupils will be able to: • read and write thousandths as decimals (3 decimal places) • represent and interpret thousandths in region, number line and place value models • recognise that 10 thousandths = 1 hundredth • write a fraction with denominator 1000 as a decimal	• Translating decimal representation to models and vice versa • Translating fraction statements and verbal statements to decimals • Relating number line representation to decimals • Applying place value concepts	• Pupil Textbook 4B, pp 21 to 27 • Practice Book 4B, pp 15 to 18 • Teacher's Guide 4B, pp 19 to 25
2	**(4) Comparing decimals** Pupils will be able to compare and order decimals. *Let's Explore!* This activity enables pupils to explore how inserting a zero in a decimal affects its value.		• Comparing • Applying place value concepts	• Pupil Textbook 4B, pp 28 to 33 • Practice Book 4B, pp 19 to 24 • Teacher's Guide 4B, pp 26 to 31

Week	Learning Objectives	Thinking Skills	Resources
2	**(5) Rounding decimals** Pupils will be able to: • round decimals to the nearest whole number • round decimals to the nearest tenth or 1 decimal place • round decimals to the nearest hundredth or 2 decimal places *Let's Explore!* These tasks enable pupils to do the reverse of rounding. They need to reverse their thinking process to find the possible numbers which can be rounded to a given value.	• Applying ordering skills and place value concepts • Applying rounding skills to practical problems	• Pupil Textbook 4B, pp 34 to 39 • Practice Book 4B, pp 25 to 30 • Teacher's Guide 4B, pp 32 to 37

Medium-term plan

Week	Learning Objectives	Thinking Skills	Resources
2–3	**(6) Fractions and decimals** Pupils will be able to: • express a fraction (whose denominator is a factor of 10 or 100) as a decimal by changing the denominator to 10 or 100 • express a decimal as a fraction in its simplest form *Maths Journal* This *Maths Journal* enables pupils to explain why the procedure Peter and Miya use in comparing decimals is incorrect.	• Applying concept of equivalent fractions • Translating fractions to decimals and vice versa • Comparing • Inductive reasoning	• Pupil Textbook 4B, pp 40 to 45 • Practice Book 4B, pp 31 to 32 • Teacher's Guide 4B, pp 38 to 43
3	*Put On Your Thinking Caps!* Pupils will be able to use tenths and hundredths for estimating lengths.	• Analysing parts and wholes • Comparing	• Pupil Textbook 4B, pp 46 to 47 • Practice Book 4B, pp 33 to 34 • Teacher's Guide 4B, pp 44 to 45

Decimals (I)

Learning objectives: Understanding tenths

Pupils will be able to:

- read and write tenths as decimals (I decimal place)
- represent and interpret tenths in region, number line and place value models
- recognise that 10 tenths = I one

- write a fraction with denominator 10 as a decimal

Key concepts

- The first decimal place represents tenths
- 10 tenths = I one

What you will need

- Circle divided into 10 equal parts (see Photocopy master I on p 233)
- Number line divided into 10 equal parts (see Photocopy master 2 on p 234)

Teaching sequence

① and ②

- Show pupils a region model (e.g. a circle) that has been divided into 10 equal parts (Photocopy master I). Ask pupils: *"What fraction of the whole is one part?"* (one tenth)
- Explain to pupils that there is another way to write $\frac{1}{10}$:

  "We write $\frac{1}{10}$ as 0·I. It is called a 'decimal' and is read as 'zero point one'." Emphasise that the value of 0·I is $\frac{1}{10}$.

- Repeat the above procedure for reading and writing the following fractions in decimal notation: $\frac{2}{10}$ (0·2) and $\frac{3}{10}$ (0·3).
- Ask pupils to derive inductively how the fractions $\frac{4}{10}, \frac{5}{10}$, etc. up to $\frac{9}{10}$ are written in decimal notation.

Unit 9 Decimals (I)

Let's Learn!

Understanding tenths

①

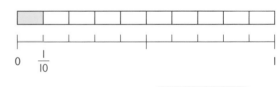

Each whole is divided into ten equal parts.

Each part is $\frac{1}{10}$ **(one-tenth)**.

We write $\frac{1}{10}$ as **0·I** as a decimal.

0·I
↑
decimal point

We read 0·I as **zero point one**. Its value is I tenth.

0·I is I tenth written as a decimal.

②

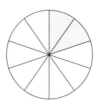

Two parts is $\frac{2}{10}$ (two-tenths).

We write $\frac{2}{10}$ as 0·2 as a decimal.

In the same way, I write $\frac{3}{10}$ as 0·3 and $\frac{4}{10}$ as 0·4.

8

Thinking skills

- Translating decimal representation to models and vice versa
- Translating fraction statements and verbal statements to decimals
- Relating number line representation to decimals
- Applying place value concepts

What you will need

- Number line (see Photocopy master 2 on p 234)
- Decimal place value chart (see Photocopy master 3 on p 235)

3 What is the decimal for each of the following?

a $\frac{5}{10}$ = [0·5]

b $\frac{6}{10}$ = [0·6]

c 3 tenths = [0·3]

d 8 tenths = [0·8]

4 What decimals do the following shaded and unshaded parts represent?

a

shaded parts = [0·4]

unshaded parts = [0·6]

b

shaded parts = [0·2]

unshaded parts = [0·8]

5 What is the decimal for each point on the number line?

0   0·1   0·2   0·3   0·4   0·5   0·6   0·7   0·8   0·9   1

6

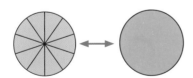

$\frac{10}{10}$ is equal to 1.

| 10 tenths = 1 one |

You can exchange 10 tenths for 1 one.

9

Teaching sequence

3

- Ask pupils to practise expressing fractions in decimal notation.

4

- This question provides pupils with more practice in reading and writing decimals for various shaded parts of region models that have been divided into 10 equal parts.

5 and **6**

- Show pupils a number line that has been divided into 10 equal parts (Photocopy master 2).
- Begin the number line with 0 and end it with 1. Help pupils to see that each part on this number line is $\frac{1}{10}$.

  So the point after 0 is 0·1 (one tenth), the next point is 0·2 (two tenths), etc.
- Ask pupils to name the other points on the number line.
- Ask pupils: "*What comes after 9 tenths?*" (10 tenths)
- Ask pupils: "*What is 10 tenths equal to?*" (1 whole)
- Show and verify that $\frac{10}{10}$ = 1 with a number line or a region model. Refer pupils to the model in example **6** of the textbook.
- Next introduce the decimal place value chart (Photocopy master 3). Use counters to demonstrate that 10 tenths can be grouped into 1 one (10 tenths = 1 one).

Unit 9: Decimals (I)   **7**

Teaching sequence

- Using the place value chart and counters, demonstrate to pupils how to write $1\frac{6}{10}$ as a decimal. Show pupils a few more examples $\left(\text{e.g. } 2\frac{4}{10}, 3\frac{7}{10}\right)$.

- Using the place value chart and counters, show pupils how to group $\frac{12}{10}$ in ones and tenths. Then write it in decimal notation: 1·2

- In the decimal 1·2, the digit 1 is in the ones place (which is immediately before the decimal point), and its value is 1.

- Emphasise that the place immediately after the decimal point is the tenths place.

- The digit 2 is in the tenths place and its value is 0·2.
  $\frac{12}{10}$ = 1 one 2 tenths
  = 1·2

- Ask pupils to group the following $\left(\text{e.g. } \frac{17}{10}, \frac{23}{10}\right)$ in ones and tenths. Then write them in decimal notation: 1·7, 2·3

9

- Ask pupils to work on this question to informally assess their understanding.

Unit 9 Decimals (1)

7 Change $1\frac{6}{10}$ to a decimal.

Ones	Tenths
○	○○○ ○○○
1	6

$1\frac{6}{10}$ = 1 one 6 tenths
     = 1·6

We read 1·6 as **one point six**.

8 Change $\frac{12}{10}$ to a decimal.

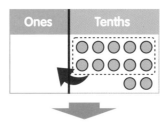

$\frac{12}{10}$ = 12 tenths

10 tenths = 1 one
12 tenths

1 one   2 tenths

Ones	Tenths
○	○○
1	2

$\frac{12}{10}$ = 1 one 2 tenths
     = 1·2

9 What is the decimal for each of the following?

   a 15 tenths = $\boxed{1\cdot5}$ **b** 2 ones 3 tenths = $\boxed{2\cdot3}$

 10

10 What decimals do the following shaded parts represent?

a

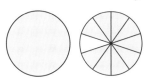

shaded parts = [1·9]

b

shaded parts = [1·5]

11 Look at the points marked with a cross (X) on the number line.
What decimals do these points represent?

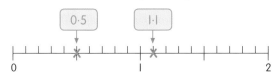

[0·5]   [1·1]

12 What is the decimal for each of the following?

a

Ones	Tenths
◯◯	◯◯◯ ◯◯

[2·5]

b

Ones	Tenths
	◯◯◯◯◯ ◯◯◯◯◯ ◯◯◯◯◯ ◯◯

[1·7]

c $2\frac{9}{10}$ = [2·9]

d $\frac{27}{10}$ = [2·7]

11

Teaching sequence

10 to **12**

• Ask pupils to work on these questions to informally assess their understanding.

- Ask pupils to work on these questions to informally assess their understanding.

Unit 9 Decimals (I)

13 Express the length of each insect as a fraction and a decimal.

a 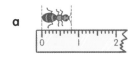　　　Length of ant = $\frac{8}{10}$ cm

= 0·8 cm

b 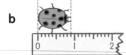　　　Length of ladybird = $\frac{9}{10}$ cm

= 0·9 cm

c 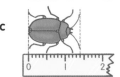　　　Length of beetle = $1\frac{4}{10}$ cm

= 1·4 cm

14 Express the total volume of water as a mixed number and a decimal.

Total volume of water = $1\frac{7}{10}\,\ell$

= 1·7 ℓ

15 What is each decimal in tenths?

a 0·2 = 2 tenths

b 0·7 = 7 tenths

c 1·1 = 11 tenths

d 1·3 = 13 tenths

12

Independent work

Practice I in Practice Book 4B,
pp 7 to 10.

Tens	Ones	Tenths
4	2	3

42·3 = 4 tens 2 ones 3 tenths

$$= 40 + 2 + 0·3$$
$$= 40 + 2 + \frac{3}{10}$$

17 Find the missing numbers.

76·4 = [7] tens [6] ones [4] tenths

$$= 70 + 6 + [0·4]$$
$$= 70 + 6 + \frac{[4]}{10}$$

18 In 23·6:

the digit 2 is in the tens place.
the digit 3 stands for 3 ones or 3.
the value of the digit 6 is 0·6.

19 Find the missing numbers.

a In 49·8, the digit [8] is in the tenths place.

b In 95·6, the digit 5 stands for [5].

c In 50·2, the value of the digit 0 is [0].

d In 92·9, the digit 9 stands for [90] and [0·9].

 Home Maths Encourage your child to point out decimal numbers when you go shopping together. Decimals can be found in the nutrition information on food labels, on price labels, on digital weighing scales and in many other places.

Practice Book 4B, p.7

13

Teaching sequence

16

- Use the place value chart to demonstrate that:
  42·3 = 4 tens 2 ones 3 tenths
  Ask pupils to write this:
  $40 + 2 + 0·3$ or $40 + 2 + \frac{3}{10}$

17

- Ask pupils to complete this question to check their ability to express a decimal in an expanded form as shown in **16** . They should express a decimal as a sum of whole numbers and fractions.

18

- Ask pupils to identify the place and value of each digit in 23·6.

19

- Ask pupils to work on this question to assess them on identifying the place and value of each digit in a number.

Learning objectives: Understanding hundredths

Pupils will be able to:

- read and write hundredths as decimals (2 decimal places)
- represent and interpret hundredths in region, number line and place value models
- recognise that 10 hundredths = 1 tenth
- write a fraction with denominator 100 as a decimal

Key concepts

- The second decimal place represents hundredths
- 10 hundredths = 1 tenth

What you will need

- Square divided into 10 equal parts (see Photocopy master 4 on p 236)
- Square divided into 100 equal parts (see Photocopy master 4 on p 236)

Teaching sequence

- Show pupils a region model (e.g. a square) that has been divided into 10 equal parts (Photocopy master 4). Ask pupils: *"What fraction of the whole is one part?"* (one tenth)
- Next show the same region model that has been divided into 100 equal parts (Photocopy master 4). Ask pupils: *"What fraction of the whole is one part?"* (one hundredth)
  When 1 whole is divided into 100 equal parts, each part is 1 hundredth of the whole.
- Write one hundredth in words and as a fraction on the board.
- Tell pupils that there is another way to write $\frac{1}{100}$: *"We write $\frac{1}{100}$ as 0·01 in decimal notation. We say 'zero point zero one'."*
- Repeat the above procedure for reading and writing the following fractions in decimal notation: $\frac{2}{100}$ (0·02) and $\frac{3}{100}$ (0·03).
- Ask pupils to derive inductively how the fractions $\frac{4}{100}$, $\frac{5}{100}$, etc. up to $\frac{9}{100}$ are written in decimal notation.

Unit 9 Decimals (1)

Let's Learn!

Understanding hundredths

1

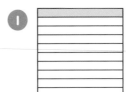 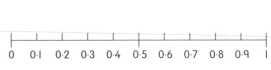

The square and the number line are each divided into ten equal parts. Each part is 1 tenth.

Divide each tenth into ten equal parts.
Now the square and the number line each have 100 equal parts.

 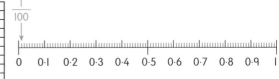

Each part is $\frac{1}{100}$ **(one hundredth)**.

We write $\frac{1}{100}$ as **0·01** as a decimal form.

$0·01 = \frac{1}{100}$
We read 0·01 as **zero point zero one**.
Its value is 1 hundredth.

In the same way, we write $\frac{2}{100}$ as 0·02 and $\frac{3}{100}$ as 0·03.

14

What you will need

- Number line divided into 10 equal parts (see Photocopy master 2 on p 234)
- Decimal place value chart (see Photocopy master 5 on p 237)

Thinking skills

- Translating decimal representation to models and vice versa
- Translating fraction statements and verbal statements to decimals
- Relating number line representation to decimals
- Applying place value concepts

2 What is the decimal for each of the following?

a $\frac{4}{100}$ g = [0·04] g

b $\frac{6}{100}$ cm = [0·06] cm

c 7 hundredths = [0·07]

d 8 hundredths = [0·08]

3 What decimals do the following shaded parts represent?

a

b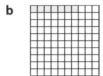

shaded parts = [0·09]

shaded parts = [0·07]

4 What is the decimal for each point on the number line?

0   0·01 0·02 0·03 0·04 0·05 0·06 0·07 0·08 0·09   0·1

5

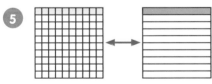

Tenths	Hundredths		Tenths	Hundredths
	⚪⚪⚪⚪⚪ ⚪⚪⚪⚪⚪		⚫	

$\frac{10}{100}$ is equal to $\frac{1}{10}$ or 0·1.

| 10 hundredths = 1 tenth |

You can exchange 10 hundredths for 1 tenth.

15

Teaching sequence

2 and **3**

- These questions provide pupils with practice on expressing hundredths in decimal notation.

4 and **5**

- Show pupils a number line that has been divided into 10 equal parts (Photocopy master 2).
- Begin the number line with 0 and end it with 0·1. Guide pupils to see that when $\frac{1}{10}$ is divided into 10 equal parts, each part is $\frac{1}{100}$. This means the point after 0 is 0·01 (one hundredth), the next point is 0·02 (two hundredths), etc.
- Ask pupils to name the other points on the number line.
- Ask pupils: "What comes after 9 hundredths?" (10 hundredths)
- Ask pupils: "What is ten hundredths $\left(\frac{10}{100}\right)$ equal to?"
- Guide pupils to see that $\frac{10}{100}$ = $\frac{1}{10}$ using the region model, the number line model and the equivalent fraction method.
- Ask pupils to write $\frac{10}{100}$ or $\frac{1}{10}$ in decimal notation (0·10 or 0·1). Guide pupils to see that 0·10 = 0·1.
- Next introduce the place value chart (Photocopy master 5). Use counters to demonstrate that 10 hundredths can be grouped into 1 tenth (10 hundredths = 1 tenth).

Teaching sequence

 and **7**

- Demonstrate using the place value chart and counters how to write 2 tenths 5 hundredths as a decimal. Show pupils a few more examples (e.g. 3 tenths 7 hundredths, 1 one 4 tenths 5 hundredths).

- Using the place value chart and counters, show pupils how to group $\frac{15}{100}$ (15 hundredths) in tenths and hundredths. Then write it in decimal notation (0·15).

- In 0·15, the digit 0 is in the ones place (which is immediately before the decimal point), and its value is 0.

- Emphasise that the place immediately after the decimal point is the tenths place. The tenths place is followed by the hundredths place.

- The digit 1 is in the tenths place and its value is 0·1. The digit 5 is in the hundredths place and its value is 0·05.

$\frac{15}{100}$ = 1 tenth 5 hundredths
      = 0·15

Emphasise to pupils that:
0·15 = 15 hundredths or
1 tenth 5 hundredths.

- Ask pupils to group the fractions $\frac{14}{100}, \frac{23}{100}, \frac{37}{100}$ in tenths and hundredths. Then write them in decimal notation (0·14, 0·23, 0·37).

- Since 0·14 = 14 hundredths, guide pupils to see that $\frac{14}{100}$ (14 hundredths) can be directly changed to the decimal 0·14. Similarly,
$\frac{23}{100}$ = 0·23 and $\frac{37}{100}$ = 0·37.
Generally, hundredths have 2 decimal places.

6 What is 2 tenths 5 hundredths written as a decimal?

Ones	Tenths	Hundredths
	○○	○○○ ○○
0	2	5

2 tenths 5 hundredths = 0·25

We read 0·25 as **zero point two five**.

7 Change $\frac{15}{100}$ to a decimal.

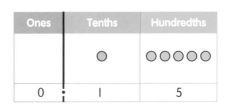

Ones	Tenths	Hundredths
		○○○○○ ○○○○○ ○○○○○

Ones	Tenths	Hundredths
	○	○○○○○
0	1	5

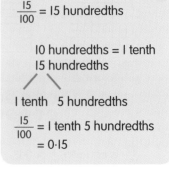

$\frac{15}{100}$ = 15 hundredths

10 hundredths = 1 tenth
15 hundredths

1 tenth   5 hundredths

$\frac{15}{100}$ = 1 tenth 5 hundredths
      = 0·15

16

8 What decimals do the following shaded parts represent?

a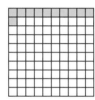

shaded parts = [0·11]

b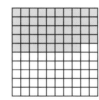

shaded parts = [0·48]

9 Look at the points marked with a cross (X) on the number line. What decimals do these points represent?

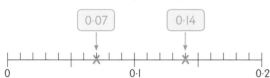

[0·07]   [0·14]

0   0·1   0·2

10 What is the decimal for each of the following?

a

Ones	Tenths	Hundredths
	◯◯◯ ◯◯	◯◯◯◯

[0·54]

b

Ones	Tenths	Hundredths
		◯◯◯◯◯ ◯◯◯◯◯ ◯◯◯◯◯ ◯◯

[0·17]

c $\frac{21}{100}$ = [0·21]   d $\frac{87}{100}$ = [0·87]

17

Teaching sequence

8 to **10**

• Ask pupils to work on these questions to informally assess their understanding.

Teaching sequence

11 to **15**

- Ask pupils to work on these questions to informally assess their understanding.

11 Does 0·9 have the same value as 0·90?

$$0·90 = \frac{90}{100}$$
$$= \frac{9}{10}$$
$$= 0·9$$

12 What is 2 ones 4 tenths 7 hundredths written as a decimal?

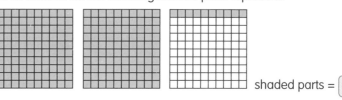

2·47

13 What decimal do the following shaded parts represent?

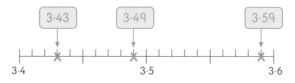

shaded parts = 2·1

14 Look at the points marked with a cross (X) on the number line. What decimals do these points represent?

3·43   3·49   3·59

15 What is the decimal for each of the following?

a

Ones	Tenths	Hundredths
●● ●	●	●●●●● ●●

3·17

b   4 ones 9 tenths 1 hundredth = 4·91

18

16 Change $1\frac{53}{100}$ to a decimal.

Ones	Tenths	Hundredths
◉	◯◯◯◯◯	◯◯◯
1	5	3

$1\frac{53}{100}$ = 1 one 5 tenths 3 hundredths
= 1·53

17 Change $\frac{147}{100}$ to a decimal.

$\frac{147}{100}$ = 1 one 47 hundredths
= 1·47

$\frac{147}{100}$ = 147 hundredths

100 hundredths = 1 one
147 hundredths

1 one   47 hundredths

18 What is the decimal for each of the following?

a $2\frac{75}{100}$ = 2·75

b $\frac{103}{100}$ = 1·03

c $3\frac{16}{100}\ell$ = 3·16 ℓ

d $\frac{204}{100}$ km = 2·04 km

19 What is each decimal in hundredths?

a   0·02 = [ ]
2 hundredths

b   0·31 = [ ]
31 hundredths

c   2·05 = [ ]
205 hundredths

20

Tens	Ones	Tenths	Hundredths
7	8	4	1

78·41 = 7 tens 8 ones 4 tenths 1 hundredth
= 70 + 8 + 0·4 + 0·01
= 70 + 8 + $\frac{4}{10}$ + $\frac{1}{100}$

19

Teaching sequence

16 and **17**

- Using the place value chart, show pupils how to group $1\frac{53}{100}$ in ones, tenths and hundredths and to change it into a decimal. Pupils can also think of $1\frac{53}{100}$ as 1 and 53 hundredths, that is, 1·53.

- Next demonstrate to pupils how to change $\frac{147}{100}$ to $1\frac{47}{100}$. Similarly,
$1\frac{47}{100}$ = 1 and 47 hundredths
= 1·47

18 and **19**

- Ask pupils to work on these questions as controlled practices.

20

- Using the place value chart, demonstrate to pupils that
78·41 = 7 tens 8 ones 4 tenths
1 hundredth
= 70 + 8 + 0·4 + 0·01
or 70 + 8 + $\frac{4}{10}$ + $\frac{1}{100}$

Teaching sequence

 21

- Ask pupils to work on this question to informally assess their understanding.

22

- Ask pupils to identify the place and value of each digit in 3·47.

23

- Ask pupils to work on this question to informally assess their understanding.

24

- Explain to pupils that since 100 pence = £1,

  1 pence = $\frac{1}{100}$ of a pound
  = £0·01

  45 pence = $\frac{45}{100}$ of a pound
  = £0·45

  60 pence = $\frac{60}{100}$ of a pound
  = £0·60

25 and **26**

- Ask pupils to work on these questions to informally assess their understanding.

Unit 9 Decimals (1)

21 Find the missing numbers.

20·39 = [2] tens [0] ones [3] tenths [9] hundredths

= 20 + 0·3 + [0·09]

= 20 + $\frac{[3]}{10}$ + $\frac{[9]}{100}$

22 In 3·47:

the digit 3 is in the ones place.
the digit 4 stands for 4 tenths or 0·4.
the value of the digit 7 is 0·07.

23 Answer these questions.

a In 5·18, the digit 1 is in the [tenths] place.

b In 2·59, the digit 9 stands for [0·09].

c In 82·03, the value of the digit 8 is [80].

24 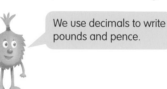 We use decimals to write pounds and pence.

£1

One pound → £1·00 = 100p

a 70p = £0·70   b 17p = £0·17   c 7p = £0·07

25 Change pence to pounds.

a 30p = £[0·30]   b 53p = £[0·53]   c 3p = £[0·03]

26 Write each amount of money as a decimal.

a 5 pounds 20 pence = £5·20   b 7 pounds 45 pence = £[7·45]

c 18 pounds = £[18·00]   d 33 pounds 5 pence = £[33·05]

20

Practice Book 4B, p.11

Learning objectives: Understanding thousandths

Pupils will be able to:

- read and write thousandths as decimals (3 decimal places)
- represent and interpret thousandths in region, number line and place value models
- recognise that 10 thousandths = 1 hundredth
- write a fraction with denominator 1000 as a decimal

Key concepts

- The third decimal place represents thousandths
- 10 thousandths = 1 hundredth

Thinking skills

- Translating decimal representation to models and vice versa
- Translating fraction statements and verbal statements to decimals
- Relating number line representation to decimals
- Applying place value concepts

What you will need

Number line models (see Photocopy master 6 on p 238)

Teaching sequence

1

- Show the number line models (Photocopy master 6): the first number line is from 0 to 1, the second number line is from 0 to 0·1, and the third number line is from 0 to 0·01.
- The first number line has been divided into 10 equal parts. Each part is 1 tenth or 0·1.
- The second number line represents 1 tenth which is divided into ten equal parts. Each part is 1 hundredth or 0·01.
- The third number line represents 1 hundredth which is divided into 10 equal parts. Each part is 1 thousandth.
- From the number lines, guide pupils to see that:
  1 part of 1 whole (divided into 10 equal parts) = 1 tenth
  1 part of 1 tenth (divided into 10 equal parts) = 1 hundredth
  1 part of 1 hundredth (divided into 10 equal parts) = 1 thousandth
- From here, guide pupils to infer that if 1 whole is divided into 1000 equal parts, each part is 1 thousandth.

2

- Show pupils a cube that has been divided into 1000 smaller cubes (e.g. a base ten 1000-block). Guide pupils to see that there are 1000 small cubes in the big block.
- Ask pupils: "*What fraction of the block is the 1 small shaded cube?*" (one thousandth). When 1 whole is divided into 1000 equal parts, each part is 1 thousandth of the whole.
- Write one thousandth in words and as a fraction on the board.
- Explain to pupils that there is another way to write $\frac{1}{1000}$: "*We write $\frac{1}{1000}$ as 0·001 in decimal notation. We say 'zero point zero zero one'.*"

Let's Learn!

Understanding thousandths

1

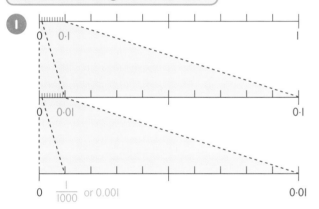

First divide 1 into ten equal parts. Each part is 1 tenth or 0·1.
Then divide 1 tenth into ten equal parts. Each part is 1 hundredth or 0·01.
Finally divide 1 hundredth into ten equal parts.

Each part is $\frac{1}{1000}$ (**one-thousandth**).

We write $\frac{1}{1000}$ as **0·001** as a decimal.

> $0·001 = \frac{1}{1000}$ or 1 thousandth
> We read 0·001 as
> **zero point zero zero one**.

2 Here is another way of showing 0·001. The shaded part is 1 cube out of 1000 cubes.

$\frac{1}{1000}$ = 1 thousandth = 0·001

21

Teaching sequence

- Ask pupils to read and write the following fractions in decimal notation: $\frac{2}{1000}$ (0·002), $\frac{3}{1000}$ (0·003), $\frac{4}{1000}$ (0·004).

- Help pupils to derive inductively how the fractions $\frac{5}{1000}$ up to $\frac{9}{1000}$ are written in decimal notation.

- Ask pupils to work on this question to assess their understanding.

5 and 6

- Show pupils a number line that has been divided into 10 equal parts (Photocopy master 2).

- Begin the number line with 0 and end it with 0·01. Guide pupils to see that when $\frac{1}{100}$ (0·01) is divided into ten equal parts, each part is $\frac{1}{1000}$. The point after 0 is 0·001 (one thousandth), the next point is 0·002 (two thousandths) and so on.

- Ask pupils to name the remaining points on the number line.

- Ask pupils: "What comes after 9 thousandths?" (10 thousandths)

- Ask pupils: "What is ten thousandths $\left(\frac{10}{1000}\right)$ equal to?" $\left(1 \text{ hundredth or } \frac{1}{100}\right)$ Encourage pupils to reduce $\frac{10}{1000}$ to $\frac{1}{100}$ by the equivalent fraction method. (10 thousandths = 1 hundredth)

- Then ask pupils to write $\frac{10}{1000}$ or $\frac{1}{100}$ in decimal notation (0·010 or 0·01). Guide pupils to see that 0·010 = 0·01.

- Next introduce this place value chart (Photocopy master 7). Use counters to demonstrate that 10 thousandths can be 'exchanged' for 1 hundredth. (10 thousandths = 1 hundredth)

What you will need

- Number line divided into 10 equal parts (see Photocopy master 2 on p 234)

- Decimal place value chart (see Photocopy master 7 on p 239)

Unit 9 Decimals (1)

3

2 thousandths

$\frac{2}{1000}$ = 2 thousandths = 0·002

In the same way $\frac{3}{1000}$ = 0·003

and $\frac{4}{1000}$ = 0·004

4 What is the decimal for each of the following?

a $\frac{5}{1000}$ 0·005   b $\frac{6}{1000}$ 0·006   c $\frac{7}{1000}$ 0·007

d 8 thousandths 0·008   e 9 thousandths 0·009

5 Work out the decimal for each point on the number line.

0 0·001 0·002 0·003 0·004 0·005 0·006 0·007 0·008 0·009 0·01

6

10 thousandths

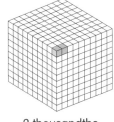

$\frac{10}{1000} = \frac{10 \div 10}{1000 \div 10} = \frac{1}{100}$ or 0·01

10 thousandths = 1 hundredth

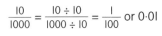

You can exchange 10 thousandths for 1 hundredth.

22

What you will need

Decimal place value chart (see Photocopy master 7 on p 239)

7 Write 3 hundredths 3 thousandths as a decimal.

Ones	Tenths	Hundredths	Thousandths
		○○○	○○○
0	0	3	3

We read 0·033 as **zero point zero three three**.

3 hundredths 3 thousandths = 0·033

8 What is the decimal for each of the following?

a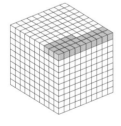

b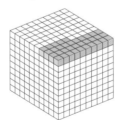

shaded parts = 0·025

shaded parts = 0·035

c

Ones	Tenths	Hundredths	Thousandths
	○	○○○ ○○○ ○○○	○○○ ○○○ ○○○

0·199

d

Ones	Tenths	Hundredths	Thousandths
			○○○○ ○○○○ ○○ ○○

0·014

10 thousandths = **1 hundredth**.

e

Ones	Tenths	Hundredths	Thousandths
○	○○○	○○ ○○ ○○ ○○	○○○○ ○○○ ○○○

1·393

23

Teaching sequence

7 and **8**

- Using the place value chart, demonstrate how to write 3 hundredths 3 thousandths as a decimal.

- Remind pupils that the second decimal place represents hundredths and the third decimal place represents thousandths.

- Ask pupils to work on **8** as a controlled practice.

Teaching sequence

- Show pupils (using the place value chart and counters) how to group $\frac{12}{1000}$ (12 thousandths) in hundredths and thousandths, and then write it in decimal notation (0·012).

- In 0·012, the digit 0 is in the ones place and tenths place. The digit 1 is in the hundredths place and its value is 0·01. The hundredths place is followed by the thousandths place. The digit 2 is in the thousandths place and its value is 0·002.

$$\frac{12}{1000} = 1 \text{ hundredth}$$
$$2 \text{ thousandths}$$
$$= 0·012$$

- Emphasise to pupils that 0·012 = 12 thousandths or 1 hundredth 2 thousandths.

- Using the place value chart and counters, ask pupils to group $\frac{112}{1000}$ in tenths, hundredths and thousandths, and then write it in decimal notation (0·112). Since 0·112 = 112 thousandths, guide pupils to see that $\frac{112}{1000}$ (112 thousandths) can be directly changed to the decimal 0·112. Similarly,

$$\frac{35}{1000} = 0·035 \text{ and}$$
$$\frac{235}{1000} = 0·235.$$

Generally, thousandths will have 3 decimal places.

- Ask pupils to change $\frac{2112}{1000}$ to a decimal in this way:

Write $\frac{2112}{1000}$ as a mixed number $2\frac{112}{1000}$. Then think of $2\frac{112}{1000}$ as 2 and 112 thousandths, i.e. 2·112.

What you will need

- Place value chart (see Photocopy master 7 on p 239)
- Counters

Unit 9 Decimals (1)

9 Change $\frac{12}{1000}$ to a decimal.

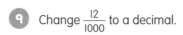

Ones	Tenths	Hundredths	Thousandths
			○○○○○ ○○○○○ ○○ ○○

$\frac{12}{1000}$ = 12 thousandths

10 thousandths = 1 hundredth
      12 thousandths

1 hundredth   2 thousandths

Ones	Tenths	Hundredths	Thousandths
		○	○○
0	0	1	2

$\frac{12}{1000}$ = 1 hundredth 2 thousandths
$= 0·012$

10 Change $\frac{112}{1000}$ to a decimal.

$\frac{112}{1000}$ = 1 tenth 12 thousandths
$\phantom{\frac{112}{1000}}$ = 1 tenth 1 hundredth 2 thousandths
$\phantom{\frac{112}{1000}}$ = 0·112

$\frac{112}{1000}$ = 112 thousandths

100 thousandths = 1 tenth
      112 thousandths

1 tenth   12 thousandths

11 Change $\frac{2112}{1000}$ to a decimal.

$\frac{2112}{1000}$ = 2 ones 112 thousandths
$\phantom{\frac{2112}{1000}}$ = 2 ones 1 tenth 1 hundredth 2 thousandths
$\phantom{\frac{2112}{1000}}$ = 2·112

$\frac{2112}{1000}$ = 2112 thousandths

2000 thousandths = 2 ones
      2112 thousandths

2 ones   112 thousandths

24

12 Change $2\frac{372}{1000}$ to a decimal.

Ones	Tenths	Hundredths	Thousandths
○○	○○○	○○○ ○○○ ○	○○
2	3	7	2

$2\frac{372}{1000}$ = 2 ones 3 tenths 7 hundredths 2 thousandths

$\qquad$ = 2·372

13 What is the decimal for each of the following?

a $\quad \frac{38}{1000}$ g = [0·038] g $\qquad$ b $\quad \frac{287}{1000}$ ml = [0·287] ml

c $\quad \frac{1001}{1000}$ km = [1·001] km $\qquad$ d $\quad 2\frac{103}{1000}$ m = [2·103] m

e $\quad 2\frac{4}{1000}$ km = [2·004] km $\qquad$ f $\quad \frac{4972}{1000}$ m = [4·972] m

g $\quad 4\frac{715}{1000}$ km = [4·715] km $\qquad$ h $\quad 2\frac{4}{1000}$ m = [2·004] m

14 Does 0·07 have the same value as 0·070? Why?

$0·07 = \frac{7}{100}$

$0·070 = \frac{70}{1000} = \frac{7}{100}$

So 0·07 and 0·070 have the same value.

25

Teaching sequence

12

- Similar to **11**, $2\frac{372}{1000}$ is 2 and 372 thousandths, i.e. 2·372.

13 and **14**

- Ask pupils to work on these questions as controlled practices.

Teaching sequence

15

- Using the place value chart, demonstrate to pupils that
  8·409 = 8 ones 4 tenths
  9 thousandths
  = 8 + 0·4 + 0·009

  Ask pupils to complete this example.

16

- Ask pupils to work on these questions to informally assess their understanding.

17

- Encourage pupils to identify the place and value of each digit in 2·315.

18

- Ask pupils to work on these questions to informally assess their understanding.

15

Ones	Tenths	Hundredths	Thousandths
8	4	0	9

8·409 = 8 ones 4 tenths 9 thousandths

$$= 8 + 0·4 + 0·009$$

$$= 8 + \frac{\boxed{4}}{10} + \frac{\boxed{9}}{1000}$$

16 Find the missing numbers.

a $7·251 = \boxed{7}$ ones $\boxed{2}$ tenths $\boxed{5}$ hundredths $\boxed{1}$ thousandth

$$= 7 + 0·2 + 0·05 + \boxed{0·001}$$

$$= 7 + \frac{\boxed{2}}{10} + \frac{\boxed{5}}{100} + \frac{\boxed{1}}{1000}$$

b $6·656 = 6 + \frac{656}{\boxed{1000}}$

17 In 2·315:

the digit 2 is in the ones place.
the digit 3 stands for 3 tenths or 0·3.
the digit 1 stands for 1 hundredth or 0·01.
the value of the digit 5 is 0·005.

18 Answer these questions.

a   In 3·465, the digit 5 is in the $\boxed{}$ place. thousandths

b   In 4·732, the digit 7 stands for $\boxed{0·7}$.

c   In 26·019, the value of the digit 1 is $\boxed{0·01}$.

26

Independent work

Practice 3 in Practice Book 4B, pp 15 to 18.

What you will need

Rectangular pieces of paper

Game

19

Players: 2
You will need:
- rectangular pieces of paper

1   Write these decimals on rectangular pieces of paper.

0·235   0·471

0·504   0·712

0·673   0·028

0·895   0·808

2   Shuffle the pieces of paper. Player I takes a piece of paper. Player 2 rewrites the decimal on it in at least two different ways.

Example

If the decimal picked was 0·813, it can be rewritten as:
- 8 tenths I hundredth 3 thousandths
- 813 thousandths
- 8 tenths 13 thousandths

3   Player I checks the answers. Take turns to play. Play four rounds each.

The player with the most correct answers wins.

Practice Book 4B, p.15

27

Teaching sequence

19 *Game*

- Ask pupils to play this game to reinforce and consolidate their understanding of using place value relationships to rename decimals.

Learning objective: Comparing decimals

Pupils will be able to compare and order decimals.

Key concept

Decimals form part of the base-ten system of numeration

Thinking skills

- Comparing
- Applying place value concepts

Teaching sequence

- Ask pupils to interpret the sub-divisions in the number line. Each sub-division represents $\frac{1}{10}$ or 0·1. 0·1 more than 0·6 is the point after 0·6, i.e. 0·7. Similarly, 0·1 less than 1·6 is the point before 1·6, i.e. 1·5.

- Alternatively, to answer the question *"What is 0·1 more than 0·6?"*, ask pupils to read the question as: *"What is 1 tenth more than 6 tenths?"* The answer is 7 tenths, i.e. 0·7.

2

- Guide pupils to see that each sub-division in the number line represents $\frac{1}{100}$ or 0·01. 0·01 more than 0·22 is the point after 0·22, i.e. 0·23. In the same way, 0·01 less than 0·18 is the point before 0·18, i.e. 0·17.

- Alternatively, to answer the question *"What is 0·01 more than 0·22?"*, ask pupils to read the question as: *"What is 1 hundredth more than 22 hundredths?"* The answer is 23 hundredths or 0·23.

Unit 9 Decimals (1)

Let's Learn!

Comparing decimals

1

0·7   1·5

0   0·5   1   1·5   2
    0·6   1·6

a What is 0·1 more than 0·6?

0·7 is 0·1 more than 0·6.

b What is 0·1 less than 1·6?

1·5 is 0·1 less than 1·6.

2

0·17   0·23

0·1   0·15   0·2   0·25   0·3
        0·18 0·22

a What is 0·01 more than 0·22?

0·23 is 0·01 more than 0·22.

b What is 0·01 less than 0·18?

0·17 is 0·01 less than 0·18.

28

3

a What is 0·001 more than 0·012?

> 0·013 is 0·001 more than 0·012.

b What is 0·001 less than 0·027?

> 0·026 is 0·001 less than 0·027.

4 Answer these questions.

a **i** What number is 0·1 more than 1·2? 1·3

  ii What number is 0·1 less than 0·9? 0·8

  iii 0·2 more than 8·7 is [8·9].

  iv 0·5 less than 4·9 is [4·4].

b **i** What number is 0·01 more than 0·15? 0·16

  ii What number is 0·01 less than 0·29? 0·28

  iii 0·02 more than 6·24 is [6·26].

  iv 0·04 less than 7·16 is [7·12].

c **i** What number is 0·001 more than 0·215? 0·216

  ii What number is 0·001 less than 0·424? 0·423

  iii 0·002 more than 4·015 is [4·017].

  iv 0·005 less than 3·147 is [3·142].

29

Teaching sequence

3

- Repeat the teaching sequence used in **2**.

  Guide pupils to see that each sub-division in the number line represents $\frac{1}{1000}$ or 0·001.

4

- Ask pupils to work on this question to informally assess their understanding.

Independent work

Practice 4 in Practice Book 4B,
pp 19 to 22.

Teaching sequence

 5

- Encourage pupils to read the number sequence as: 2 tenths, 4 tenths, 6 tenths, 8 tenths. Ask pupils what the next decimal after 8 tenths should be. From the pattern, pupils should answer 10 tenths or 1. Ask pupils to predict the next two decimals in tenths, that is, 12 tenths and 14 tenths or 1·2 and 1·4.

 6

- Encourage pupils to read the number sequence as:
  1 and 12 hundredths,
  1 and 17 hundredths,
  1 and 22 hundredths,
  1 and 27 hundredths,
  1 and 32 hundredths.

- Ask pupils for the increase in hundredths, i.e. 5 hundredths. Therefore, the next two decimals are 1 and 37 hundredths (1·37) and 1 and 42 hundredths (1·42).

 7

- Read the number sequence as:
  1 and 464 thousandths,
  1 and 462 thousandths,
  1 and 460 thousandths,
  1 and 458 thousandths,
  1 and 456 thousandths.

- Ask pupils to state the decrease in thousandths and to predict the next two decimals.

Unit 9 Decimals (1)

5 These decimals are arranged in a pattern.

0·2, 0·4, 0·6, 0·8, 1·0, …

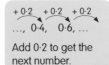

..., 0·4, 0·6, ...
+0·2 +0·2 +0·2
Add 0·2 to get the next number.

What are the next two decimals? 1·2, 1·4

6 These decimals are arranged in a pattern.

1·12, 1·17, 1·22, 1·27, 1·32, …

..., 1·17, 1·22, ...
+0·05 +0·05 +0·05
Add 0·05 to get the next number.

What are the next two decimals? 1·37, 1·42

7 These decimals are arranged in a pattern.

1·464, 1·462, 1·460, 1·458, 1·456, …

..., 1·464, 1·462, ...
−0·002 −0·002 −0·002
Subtract 0·002 to get the next number.

What are the next two decimals? 1·454, 1·452

Practice Book 4B, p.19

30

What you will need

Decimal place value chart
(see Photocopy master 7 on
p 239)

Decimals (I) **Unit 9**

8 Which is greater, 0·4 or 0·34?

Ones	Tenths	Hundredths
0	4	
0	3	4

In the same way as comparing whole numbers, we start from the left.

First compare the **ones**. They are the same.
Then compare the **tenths**.
4 tenths is greater than 3 tenths.
So 0·4 is **greater than** 0·34.

9 Arrange 0·62, 0·263 and 0·6 in order. Begin with the smallest.

Ones	Tenths	Hundredths	Thousandths
0	6	2	
0	2	6	3
0	6		

First compare the **ones**.
They are the same.
Then compare the **tenths**.
6 tenths is greater than 2 tenths.
So 0·263 is the smallest.

As 0·62 and 0·6 have the same tenths, compare the **hundredths**.
2 hundredths is greater than 0 hundredths.
So 0·62 is greater than 0·6.
The order beginning with the smallest is 0·263, 0·6, 0·62.

10 Which is greater?

a   0·76 or 0·8 0·8   b   0·4 or 0·234 0·4

c   0·012 or 0·12 0·12   d   0·303 or 0·33 0·33

11 Arrange the decimals in order. Begin with the smallest.

a   0·8, 0·17, 0·315 0·17, 0·315, 0·8

b   0·18, 0·2, 0·185 0·18, 0·185, 0·2

You can use place value charts to help you compare these decimals.

c   1·004, 0·04, 0·104 0·04, 0·104, 1·004

d   0·202, 0·022, 0·22 0·022, 0·202, 0·22

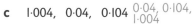
Practice Book 4B, p.23

31

- Show pupils the place value chart (Photocopy master 7). Explain to pupils that decimals are also part of the base-ten system of numeration.

- Explain to pupils that since decimals are part of the base-ten system of numeration, they can be compared like whole numbers, i.e. by comparing the digits place by place starting from the left.

- Using the place value chart, demonstrate the process of comparing decimals (e.g. 0·4 and 0·34).

- Compare the whole number parts first. Since the whole number parts are the same, we then compare the decimal parts.

- Guide pupils to see that the tenths digit in 0·4 is greater than the tenths digit in 0·34. This means 0·4 is greater than 0·34.
Compare the digits of 0·62, 0·263 and 0·6 starting from the left in the same way.

10 and **11**

- Ask pupils to compare the decimals in these questions to informally assess their understanding.

Unit 9: Decimals (I)   **29**

Teaching sequence

12 and **13** *Games*

- Ask pupils to play these games to reinforce and consolidate their skill in comparing decimals and arranging decimals in order.

Game

12 How to play:

Players: 2
You will need:
- 12 cards

1   Make a set of cards using these decimals:

0·5	0·05	0·6	0·07
0·17	1·7	0·71	0·16
1·5	1·06	1·61	0·76

2   Shuffle the cards. Player I takes 3 cards. They arrange the decimals in order, beginning with the smallest. Player 2 checks the answer.

3   Return the card to the pack and shuffle it. Take turns to play. Play three rounds each.

The player with the most correct answers wins.

Game

13 How to play:

Players: 3

I can choose any decimal between 0 and I except 0·001 and 0·999.

1   Player I thinks of a decimal between 0 and I. They tell the other players the decimal.

2   Player 2 says a decimal between 0 and I that is greater than Player I's decimal.

3   Player 3 says a decimal between 0 and I that is smaller than the first player's decimal.

Take turns to think of a decimal between 0 and I. Play two rounds each. At each round, the players discuss their answers.

32

Objective of activity

This activity enables pupils to explore how inserting a zero in a decimal affects its value.

Let's Explore!

14 Your teacher will give you a decimal (for example, 2·58).

I   Insert a zero at any place in this decimal (for example, 2·058).

2   Compare the decimal you made with the original decimal. Then say whether it is greater than, smaller than or equal to the original decimal.

Ones	Tenths	Hundredths	Thousandths
2	5	8	
2	0	5	8

2·058 is smaller than 2·58.

3   Next insert the zero in a different place (for example, 2·580). Then say whether the number is greater than, smaller than or equal to the original decimal.

4   Repeat step 3 until you have inserted a zero in all the different possible places in the original decimal.

Discuss with your friends how inserting a zero into different places in a decimal changes its value.

33

Teaching sequence

14 *Let's Explore!*

• This activity enables pupils to explore how inserting a zero in a decimal affects its value. Guide pupils to deduce that the smallest value is obtained when the zero is placed just after the decimal point and the value is unchanged when the zero is placed at the end of the decimal.

Learning objectives: Rounding decimals

Pupils will be able to:

- round decimals to the nearest whole number
- round decimals to the nearest tenth or 1 decimal place
- round decimals to the nearest hundredth or 2 decimal places

Key concepts

- Between two consecutive whole numbers, there are 10 tenths
- Between two consecutive tenths, there are 10 hundredths
- Between two consecutive hundredths, there are 10 thousandths

Teaching sequence

- Show pupils how to round a decimal to the nearest whole number. Explain that this means finding the whole number which is nearest to the decimal.
  Use a number line to help pupils understand the rounding process.
- Ask pupils "*What are the two nearest whole numbers between which 8·6 lies?*" (8 and 9)
- Draw a number line beginning with 8 and ending with 9. Lead pupils to see that between 8 and 9, there are 10 tenths and so, 8·1, 8·2, 8·3, 8·4, 8·5, 8·6, 8·7, 8·8 and 8·9 will be between 8 and 9. Ask pupils to mark the decimal 8·6 on the number line.
- Ask pupils "*Is 8·6 nearer to 8 or to 9?*"

- Repeat the procedure used in ❶ for this example.

Unit 9 Decimals (I)

Let's Learn!

Rounding decimals

 ❶

The height of a statue is about 8·6 m. Round 8·6 to the nearest whole number.

8·6

| | | | | | | | | | | |

8   8·5   9

8·6 is between 8 and 9.
It is nearer to 9 than to 8.
8·6 is 9 when rounded to the nearest whole number.
So 8·6 ≈ 9.

❷   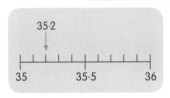 The mass of these potatoes is 35·2 kg. What is their mass to the nearest kilogram?

35·2 kg ≈ 35 kg

35·2

| | | | | | | | | | |

35   35·5   36

35·2 is between 35 and 36. It is nearer to 35 than to 36.
35·2 is 35 when rounded to the nearest whole number.
So 35·2 ≈ 35.
The mass of potatoes to the nearest kilogram is 35 kg.

34

3 Round 26·5 to the nearest whole number.

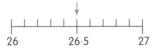

26·5 is exactly halfway between 26 and 27.
We round it to 27.
26·5 is 27 when rounded to the nearest whole number.
So 26·5 ≈ 27.

4 Round 14·68 to the nearest whole number.

14·68 is between 14 and 15. It is nearer to 15 than to 14.
14·68 is 15 when rounded to the nearest whole number.
So 14·68 ≈ 15.

5 Round 39·45 to the nearest whole number.

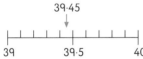

39·45 is between 39 and 40. It is nearer to 39 than to 40.
39·45 is 39 when rounded to the nearest whole number.
So 39·45 ≈ 39.

6 For each decimal, draw a number line. Use a cross (X) to show where the decimal is on the number line. Then round it to the nearest whole number.

Example

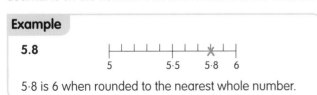

5·8 is 6 when rounded to the nearest whole number.

a 0·45 0   **b** 0·7 1   **c** 4·3 4   **d** 12·5 13

Practice Book 4B, p.25   35

Thinking skills

- Applying ordering skills and place value concepts
- Applying rounding skills to practical problems

Independent work

Practice 6 in Practice Book 4B, pp 25 to 26.

Teaching sequence

- Guide pupils to see that when a decimal is exactly halfway between two consecutive whole numbers, it is rounded to the greater number (e.g. 26·5 is 27 when rounded to the nearest whole number).

- Guide pupils to see that when a number with 2 decimal places is rounded to the nearest whole number, it is the tenths digit which determines which whole number it is rounded to. In 14·68, since 14·6 is nearer to 15 than to 14, 14·68 must be even nearer to 15. So 14·68 is rounded to 15.

5

- In 39·45, 39·4 is nearer to 39 than to 40. Though 39·45 is greater than 39·4, it is less than 39·5. So 39·45 is still nearer to 39. Therefore 39·45 is rounded to 39.

- Ask pupils to work on this question to informally assess their understanding.

Teaching sequence

- Show pupils how to round decimals to the nearest tenth or 1 decimal place. This means finding a 1-place decimal nearest to the given decimal.
- To round 0·83 to the nearest tenth or 1 decimal place, ask pupils what the two nearest tenths to 0·83 are.
- Guide pupils to see that between 0·8 and 0·9, there are 10 hundredths and so 0·81, 0·82, 0·83, 0·84, 0·85, 0·86, 0·87, 0·88 and 0·89 are between 0·8 and 0·9.
- Using the number line from 0·8 to 0·9, ask pupils to show you where 0·83 is.
- Ask pupils "*Is 0·83 nearer to 0·8 or to 0·9?*" (0·8)

8

- Explain to pupils that when a decimal is exactly halfway between two consecutive tenths, it is rounded to the greater tenth. 1·75 rounded to the nearest tenth (or 1 decimal place) is 1·8.

9

- Tell pupils that when a decimal is rounded to 1 decimal place and the result is a whole number, a 0 in the tenths place must be included after the decimal point.

10

- Ask pupils to work on this exercise to informally assess their understanding.

Unit 9 Decimals (1)

7 Liam's height is 0·83 m. Round 0·83 to the nearest tenth or 1 decimal place.

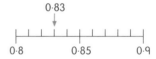

0·83 = 8 tenths 3 hundredths
0·83 is between 8 tenths (0·8) and 9 tenths (0·9).
It is nearer to 0·8 than to 0·9.
0·83 is 0·8 when rounded to the nearest tenth or 1 decimal place.
So 0·83 ≈ 0·8.

8 Round 1·75 to the nearest tenth.

1·75 is exactly halfway between 1·7 and 1·8.
We round it to 1·8.
1·75 is 1·8 when rounded to the nearest tenth.
So 1·75 ≈ 1·8.

9 Round 2·98 to 1 decimal place.

2·98 is between 2·9 and 3.
It is nearer to 3 than to 2·9.
2·98 is 3·0 when rounded to 1 decimal place.
So 2·98 ≈ 3·0.

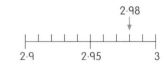

> 3 is written as 3·0 to 1 decimal place.

10 For each decimal, draw a number line. Use a cross (X) to show where the decimal is on the number line. Then round it to 1 decimal place.

Example

3·43

3·43 is 3·4 when rounded to 1 decimal place.

a 0·36 0·4   **b** 4·32 4·3   **c** 4·05 4·1

36

What you will need

Number line (see Photocopy master 2 on p 234)

11 A sheet of plastic is 0·014 cm thick. Round 0·014 to the nearest hundredth or 2 decimal places.

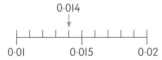

0·014 = I hundredth 4 thousandths
0·014 is between I hundredth (0·01) and 2 hundredths (0·02).
It is nearer to 0·01 than to 0·02.
0·014 is 0·01 when rounded to the nearest hundredth or 2 decimal places.
So 0·014 ≈ 0·01.

12 Round 2·345 to the nearest hundredth.

2·345 is exactly halfway between 2·34 and 2·35.
We round it to 2·35.
2·345 is 2·35 when rounded to the nearest hundredth.
So 2·345 ≈ 2·35.

13 Round 5·997 to 2 decimal places.

5·997 is between 5·99 and 6.
It is nearer to 6 than to 5·99.
5·997 is 6·00 when rounded to 2 decimal places.
So 5·997 ≈ 6·00.

> 6 is written as 6·00 to 2 decimal places.

14 For each decimal, draw a number line. Use a cross (X) to show where the decimal is on the number line. Then round it to 2 decimal places.

Example

0·123

0·123 is 0·12 when rounded to 2 decimal places.

a 0·516 0·52   **b** 3·294 3·29   **c** 8·995 9·00

37

Teaching sequence

11 to **13**

- For these examples, repeat the teaching sequence for rounding decimals to the nearest hundredth or 2 decimal places. For **11**, help pupils to see that 0·014 is between 0·01 and 0·02, and there are 10 thousandths between 0·01 and 0·02.

- Draw a number line from 0·01 to 0·02 and ask pupils to mark the thousandths from 0·011 to 0·019 on it.

- Ask pupils "Is 0·014 nearer to 0·01 or to 0·02?"

14

- Ask pupils to work on this question as a controlled practice.

Independent work

Practice 7 in Practice Book 4B,
pp 27 to 30.

Teaching sequence

- Ask pupils to work on this
  question to informally assess
  their understanding.

 a   Round the following decimals to the nearest whole number, nearest
tenth and nearest hundredth.

Decimal	Rounded to the Nearest		
	Whole Number	Tenth	Hundredth
2·029	2	2·0	2·03
5·783	6	5·8	5·78

b   Round the following decimals to the nearest whole number,
I decimal place and 2 decimal places.

Decimal	Rounded to		
	The Nearest Whole Number	I Decimal Place	2 Decimal Places
12·705	13	12·7	12·71
25·957	26	26·0	25·96

Practice Book 4B, p.27

38

Objective of activity

These tasks enable pupils to do the reverse of rounding. They need to reverse their thinking process to find the possible numbers which can be rounded to a given value.

Activity

16 Work in pairs.
You have £25·00. You want to buy these items at a supermarket.
Round the cost of each item to I decimal place.
Then add to find out whether you have enough money to pay for the items.

£2·49   £6·45   £2·95
£7·45

3 + 2·5 + 6·5 + 3 + 7·5 + 2 = 24·5
The total cost is about £24·50 so there
is enough money to pay for the items.

£2·99   £1·98

Let's Explore!

17 **Example**

A number has 2 decimal places. It is I·7 when rounded to I decimal place. What could the number be?

Tai draws a number line to find the number.

| I·63 | I·64 | I·65 | I·66 | I·67 | I·68 | I·69 | I·70 | I·71 | I·72 | I·73 | I·74 | I·75 | I·76 |

The numbers in blue are the possible answers.

A number has 3 decimal places. It is 2·34 when rounded to 2 decimal places.

    2·335, 2·336,
    2·337, 2·338,
a What could the number be? List the possible answers. 2·339, 2·340,
b Which of these numbers is the greatest? 2·344   2·341, 2·342,
c Which of these numbers is the smallest? 2·335   2·343, 2·344

39

Teaching sequence

● This activity enables pupils to consolidate their skills in rounding by applying them to practical situations.

17 *Let's Explore!*

● This exploratory activity requires pupils to do the reverse of the process of rounding. A number with 2 decimal places gives I·7 when rounded to the nearest tenth. It enables pupils to reverse their thinking process by asking what the possible 2-place decimals that will round to I·7 are.

● Next ask pupils to explore using the same principle for numbers with 3 decimal places.

● Encourage pupils to note that 2·34 is the same as 2·340. Ask them to draw a number line and mark at least 6 decimals greater than and 6 decimals smaller than 2·340 at intervals of 0·00I to help them find the answers for **b** and **c**.

Learning objectives: Fractions and decimals

Pupils will be able to:

- express a fraction (whose denominator is a factor of 10 or 100) as a decimal by changing the denominator to 10 or 100
- express a decimal as a fraction in its simplest form

Key concept

Decimals up to 3 places are fractions with denominators 10, 100, 1000.

Teaching sequence

- Show pupils how to write a fraction $\left(\text{e.g. } \dfrac{1}{5}\right)$ as a decimal by first changing the denominator to 10. Find the equivalent fraction of $\dfrac{1}{5}$ that has the denominator 10 $\left(\dfrac{1}{5} = \dfrac{2}{10}\right)$. $\dfrac{2}{10}$ is 0·2 in decimal notation. So $\dfrac{1}{5}$ is 0·2 as a decimal.

- Show pupils the fraction bar and number line in the textbook. From these models, pupils can see that $\dfrac{1}{5} = 0{\cdot}2$.

- Next show pupils how to write a fraction $\left(\text{e.g. } \dfrac{1}{4}\right)$ as a decimal by first converting the denominator to 100.
- Find the equivalent fraction of $\dfrac{1}{4}$ that has the denominator 100 $\left(\dfrac{1}{4} = \dfrac{25}{100}\right)$. $\dfrac{25}{100}$ is 0·25 in decimal notation. So $\dfrac{1}{4}$ is 0·25 as a decimal.

Unit 9 Decimals (1)

Let's Learn!

Fractions and decimals

1 Express the fraction $\dfrac{1}{5}$ as a decimal.

$$\dfrac{1}{5} \; \overset{\times 2}{\underset{\times 2}{=}} \; \dfrac{2}{10} = 0{\cdot}2$$

> Convert the denominator 5 to 10.

So $\dfrac{1}{5}$ is 0·2 as a decimal.

2 Here is another way to show $\dfrac{1}{5} = 0{\cdot}2$.

Look at the fraction bar and the number line.

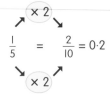

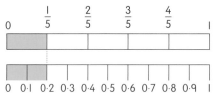

3 Express $\dfrac{1}{4}$ as a decimal.

$$\dfrac{1}{4} \; \overset{\times 25}{\underset{\times 25}{=}} \; \dfrac{25}{100} = 0{\cdot}25$$

> Can you convert the denominator 4 to 10?

> No, but I can convert it to 100.

So $\dfrac{1}{4}$ is 0·25 as a decimal.

40

Thinking skills
- Applying concept of equivalent fractions
- Translating fractions to decimals and vice versa
- Comparing
- Inductive reasoning

Decimals (I) **Unit 9**

4 You can see that $\frac{1}{4} = 0.25$.

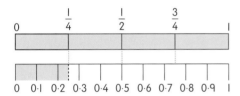

You can also see that
$\frac{1}{2} = \boxed{0.5}$ and $\frac{3}{4} = \boxed{0.75}$.

5 Express $\frac{5}{4}$ as a decimal.

$\frac{5}{4} = \frac{4}{4} + \frac{1}{4}$

$\quad = 1 + \frac{1}{4}$

$\quad = 1 + 0.25$

$\quad = 1.25$

$\frac{1}{4} = \frac{25}{100}$ so $\frac{1}{4}$ is 0.25.

6 Express $\frac{8}{5}$ as a decimal.

$\frac{8}{5} = \frac{5}{5} + \frac{\boxed{3}}{5}$

$\quad = 1 + \boxed{0.6}$

$\quad = \boxed{1.6}$

7 Express each fraction as a decimal.

a $\frac{3}{5}$ 0.6   b $\frac{5}{2}$ 2.5   c $\frac{9}{20}$ 0.45

d $\frac{3}{2}$ 1.5   e $\frac{7}{5}$ 1.4   f $\frac{11}{4}$ 2.75

41

Teaching sequence

4

- Show pupils the fraction bar and number line in the textbook. From these models, pupils can see that $\frac{1}{4} = 0.25$.

5

- Show pupils how to change an improper fraction to a decimal.
- Express the improper fraction as a whole number and a fraction. Then convert the proper fraction to a decimal.

6

- Ask pupils to work on this question as a controlled practice.

7

- Ask pupils to express the fractions as decimals to informally assess their understanding.
- From the above examples, guide pupils to see that a fraction (whose denominator is a factor of 10 or 100) can be expressed as a decimal by first changing the denominator to 10 or 100.

Teaching sequence

8

- Show pupils how to write a mixed number $\left(\text{e.g. } 3\frac{1}{2}\right)$ as a decimal. Guide pupils to see that they need only change the fraction to a decimal, while leaving the whole number unchanged:

  In $3\frac{1}{2}$, the fraction is $\frac{1}{2}$.

  Find the equivalent fraction of $\frac{1}{2}$ that has the denominator 10 or 100 $\left(\frac{1}{2} = \frac{5}{10}\right)$.

  $\frac{5}{10}$ is 0·5 in decimal notation.

  So $3\frac{1}{2}$ is $3 + 0·5 = 3·5$.

- Alternatively, express $3\frac{1}{2}$ as an improper fraction, i.e. $\frac{7}{2}$.

  Then rename $\frac{7}{2}$ as $\frac{35}{10}$, which is equal to 3·5.

9

- Ask pupils to express the mixed numbers as decimals to informally assess their understanding.

10

- Review with pupils that decimals represent tenths, hundredths and thousandths.

  So $0·8 = \frac{8}{10} = \frac{4}{5}$.

Unit 9 Decimals (I)

8 Express $3\frac{1}{2}$ as a decimal.

The whole number 3 remains unchanged.

But change the fraction $\frac{1}{2}$ to a decimal.

$$\times 5$$

$$\frac{1}{2} \quad = \quad \frac{5}{10} = 0·5$$

$$\times 5$$

$$3\frac{1}{2} = \frac{7}{2}$$
$$= \frac{7 \times 5}{2 \times 5}$$
$$= \frac{35}{10}$$
$$= 3·5$$

This is another method to express a mixed number as a decimal.

$3\frac{1}{2}$ is 3·5 as a decimal.

9 Express each mixed number as a decimal.

a $2\frac{3}{5}$ 2·6   b $9\frac{1}{4}$ 9·25   c $1\frac{8}{20}$ 1·4   d $5\frac{27}{50}$ 5·54

10 Express 0·8 as a fraction in its simplest form.

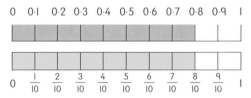

0   0·1   0·2   0·3   0·4   0·5   0·6   0·7   0·8   0·9   1

0   $\frac{1}{10}$ $\frac{2}{10}$ $\frac{3}{10}$ $\frac{4}{10}$ $\frac{5}{10}$ $\frac{6}{10}$ $\frac{7}{10}$ $\frac{8}{10}$ $\frac{9}{10}$ 1

$$0·8 = \frac{8}{10}$$
$$= \frac{4}{5}$$

Divide the numerator and denominator by 2.

42

Practice 8 in Practice Book 4B,
pp 3l to 32.

11 Express 2·5 as a mixed number in its simplest form.

$2·5 = \frac{25}{10}$

$= \frac{20}{10} + \frac{5}{10}$

> Divide the numerator and denominator of $\frac{5}{10}$ by 5.

$= 2 + \frac{5}{10}$

$= 2 + \frac{1}{2}$

$= 2\frac{1}{2}$

12 Express 7·25 as a mixed number in its simplest form.

$7·25 = 7 + 0·25$

> $\frac{25}{100} = \frac{5}{20} = \frac{1}{4}$

$= 7 + \frac{25}{100}$

$= 7 + \frac{1}{4}$

$= 7\frac{1}{4}$

13 Express each decimal as a fraction or a mixed number in its simplest form.

a $0·4 \quad \frac{2}{5}$ b $2·8 \quad 2\frac{4}{5}$ c $3·75 \quad 3\frac{3}{4}$

d $0·6 \quad \frac{3}{5}$ e $5·2 \quad 5\frac{1}{5}$ f $2·45 \quad 2\frac{9}{20}$

g $2·75 \quad 2\frac{3}{4}$ h $4·35 \quad 4\frac{7}{20}$ i $8·72 \quad 8\frac{18}{25}$

> Practice Book 4B, p.3I

43

Teaching sequence

11 and **12**

- To express a decimal as a mixed number, show pupils the method given in the textbook. Alternatively, guide pupils to see that,

  $2·5 = 2\frac{5}{10} = 2\frac{1}{2}$ and

  $7·25 = 7\frac{25}{100} = 7\frac{1}{4}$

- Similarly, $1·125 = 1\frac{125}{1000}$.

  Remind pupils to reduce the fraction to its simplest form.

13

- Ask pupils to work on this question to informally assess their understanding.

What you will need

Decimal and fraction cards (see Photocopy master 8 on pp 240 to 243)

Teaching sequence

 Game

- Ask pupils to play the game 'Snap a decimal!' to reinforce and consolidate their ability to recognise fraction and decimal equivalents.

Unit 9 Decimals (I)

Game

14 **Snap a decimal!**

How to play:

Players: 4 or 5
You will need:
- decimal cards
- fraction cards

1 Put all the decimal cards face up on a table.

2 Shuffle the fraction cards. Then turn over the fraction card at the top of the pack.

3 Check if the fraction on the card shown is equivalent to any of the decimals on the table.

> For example, the fraction $\frac{1}{5}$ is equivalent to the decimal 0·2.

4 The fastest player to find a match calls out "decimal snap", and collects the two cards.

The other players check the answer. If the answer is wrong, the cards are taken away from the player and put back on the table and at the bottom of the fraction cards pack.

5 Turn over the next fraction card to continue the game. Play until no more matches can be found.

> The player who collects the most matching cards wins.

44

Unit 9: Decimals (I)

Objective of activity

This *Maths Journal* enables pupils to explain why the procedure Peter and Miya use in comparing decimals is incorrect.

Maths Journal

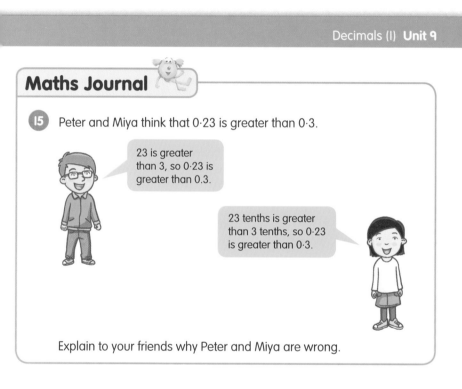

15 Peter and Miya think that 0·23 is greater than 0·3.

23 is greater than 3, so 0·23 is greater than 0.3.

23 tenths is greater than 3 tenths, so 0·23 is greater than 0·3.

Explain to your friends why Peter and Miya are wrong.

Teaching sequence

15 *Maths Journal*

- This task encourages pupils to express their understanding of decimals by explaining why the thinking processes used to compare the decimals shown are incorrect.

45

Objective of activities

These tasks enable pupils to use tenths and hundredths for estimating lengths.

Independent work

Challenging Practice and *Problem Solving* in Practice Book 4B, pp 33 to 34.

Thinking skills

- Analysing parts and wholes
- Comparing

What you will need

Paper strips (see Photocopy master 9 on p 244)

Teaching sequence

16 *Put On Your Thinking Caps!*

- This activity enables pupils to apply their conceptual understanding of tenths. Give each pupil a strip of paper (Photocopy master 9).
- Tell pupils to think of the paper strip as a number line from 0 to 1. If the paper strip is divided into 10 equal parts, each part will be equal to 0·1 units. So the number line will start with 0, the next marking will be 0·1, 0·2 ... 0·9, and it will end with 1.
- Then pupils should use the paper strip to estimate in tenths the length of the given lines.

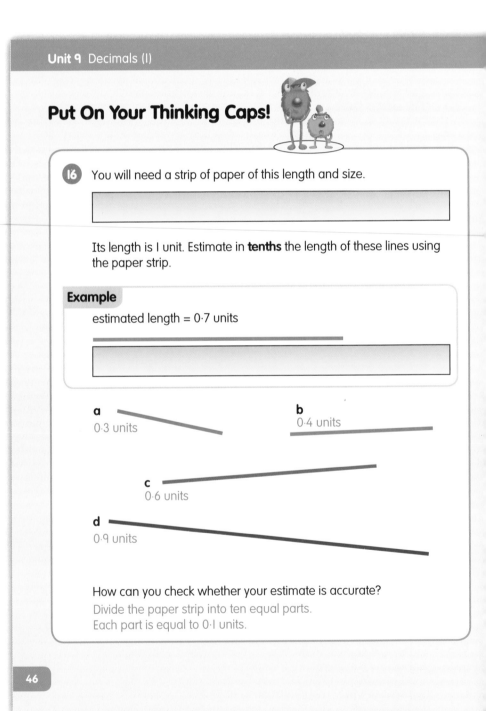

Unit 9 Decimals (1)

Put On Your Thinking Caps!

16 You will need a strip of paper of this length and size.

Its length is 1 unit. Estimate in **tenths** the length of these lines using the paper strip.

Example

estimated length = 0·7 units

a
0·3 units

b
0·4 units

c
0·6 units

d
0·9 units

How can you check whether your estimate is accurate?
Divide the paper strip into ten equal parts.
Each part is equal to 0·1 units.

46

What you will need
Paper strips with markings (see
Photocopy master 9 on p 244)

Decimals (I) **Unit 9**

Put On Your Thinking Caps!

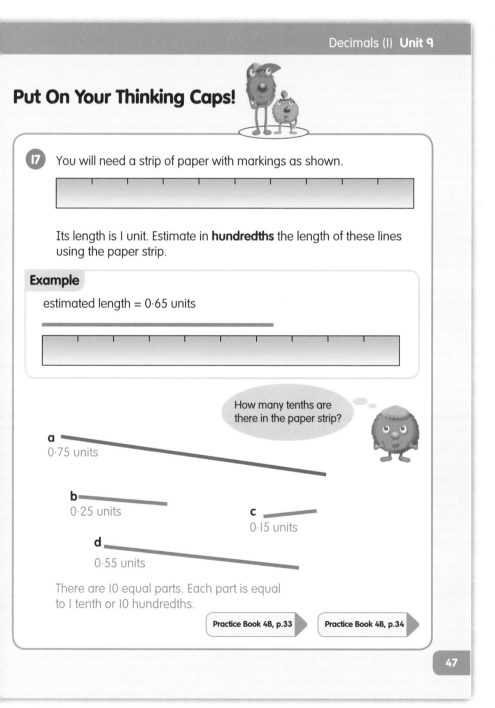

17 You will need a strip of paper with markings as shown.

Its length is I unit. Estimate in **hundredths** the length of these lines
using the paper strip.

Example

estimated length = 0·65 units

How many tenths are
there in the paper strip?

a
0·75 units

b
0·25 units

c
0·15 units

d
0·55 units

There are 10 equal parts. Each part is equal
to I tenth or 10 hundredths.

Practice Book 4B, p.33   Practice Book 4B, p.34

47

Teaching sequence

17 *Put On Your Thinking Caps!*

- This activity enables pupils
  to apply their conceptual
  understanding of hundredths.
  Give each pupil a strip
  of paper with markings
  (Photocopy master 9).

- Tell pupils to think of the
  paper strip as a number line
  from 0 to I. If the paper strip
  is divided into I0 equal parts,
  each part will be equal to 0·I
  units. So the number line will
  start with 0, the next marking
  will be 0·I, 0·2 ... 0·9, and it
  will end with I.

- Ask pupils to visualise the
  hundredths when each part
  (0·I units) is further divided
  into I0 equal parts.

- Then pupils should use the
  paper strip to estimate in
  hundredths the length of the
  given lines.

Unit 9 Decimals (I)

Date: _____

Practice I Understanding tenths

1 Colour the square(s) to represent the decimal. Each square represents I whole.

a

0·6

b

1·8

c

0·3

d

1·5

2 Write as a decimal.

a

Ones	Tenths
○	○ ○ ○

0·3

b

Ones	Tenths
○ ○	○ ○

2·2

c

Ones	Tenths
○ ○ ○ ○	○ ○ ○ ○ ○ ○

4·6

d

Ones	Tenths
○ ○ ○ ○ ○	○ ○ ○ ○ ○ ○ ○

5·7

Unit 9: Decimals (I)

7

INSPIRE
MATHS

PRACTICE BOOK 4B

Koogol
Googol
Zoogol
Toogol
Noogol
Ooogol

Consultant and author
Dr Fong Ho Kheong

Authors
Chelvi Ramakrishnan and Gan Kee Soon

UK consultants
Carole Skinner, Simon d'Angelo and Elizabeth Gibbs

3 Write as a decimal.

a 9 tenths = 0.9

b 13 tenths = 1.3

c 26 tenths = 2.6

d 123 tenths = 12.3

4 Write as a decimal.

a $\frac{7}{10}$ = 0.7

b $2\frac{3}{10}$ = 2.3

c $\frac{41}{10}$ = 4.1

d $\frac{109}{10}$ = 10.9

5 Write the value of each decimal in tenths.

a 2.3 = 23 tenths

b 5.6 = 56 tenths

c 26.5 = 265 tenths

d 48.4 = 484 tenths

6 Use a cross (X) to show where each decimal is on the number line.

a 0.9   b 1.6   c 1.8   d 2.4

7 Write the correct decimal in each box. The first one has been done for you.

0.4   1.2   1.9   2.7

8 Write as a fraction and a decimal.

a

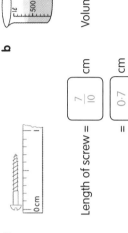

Length of screw = $\frac{7}{10}$ cm

= 0.7 cm

b

Volume of water = $\frac{6}{10}$ ℓ

= 0.6 ℓ

9 Write as a mixed number and a decimal.

a

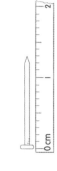

Length of nail = $1\frac{3}{10}$ cm

= 1.3 cm

b

Volume of water = $2\frac{4}{10}$ ℓ

= 2.4 ℓ

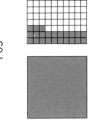

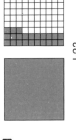

Date: _____

Practice 2   Understanding hundredths

1 Colour the square(s) to represent the decimal. Each large square represents 1 whole.

a

0.06

b

1.05

c

0.55

d

1.23

2 Write as a decimal.

a

Ones	Tenths	Hundredths

0.36

b

Ones	Tenths	Hundredths

2.05

c

Ones	Tenths	Hundredths

4.5

d

Ones	Tenths	Hundredths

5.68

---

10 Fill in the spaces.

a   3.4 = 3 ones ___4___ tenths

b   5.8 = ___5___ ones 8 tenths

c   22.1 = 2 tens 2 ones ___1___ tenth

d   36.7 = ___3___ tens 6 ones 7 tenths

11 15.2 can be written as $10 + 5 + \frac{2}{10}$. Fill in the boxes in the same way.

a $4.5 = \boxed{4} + \boxed{\frac{5}{10}}$

b $23.7 = \boxed{20} + \boxed{3} + \boxed{\frac{7}{10}}$

12 14.3 can be written as $10 + 4 + 0.3$. Fill in the boxes in the same way.

a $6.9 = \boxed{6} + \boxed{0.9}$

b $34.4 = \boxed{30} + \boxed{4} + \boxed{0.4}$

13 Fill in the spaces.

a

Tens	Ones	Tenths
3	4	6

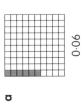

The digit 6 is in the ___tenths___ place. Its value is ___0.6___ .

b

Tens	Ones	Tenths
5	0	8

The digit 8 is in the ___tenths___ place. Its value is ___0.8___ .

7 Use a cross (X) to show where each decimal is on the number line.

a 0·02   b 0·14   c 0·22   d 0·27

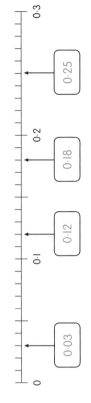

8 Write the correct decimal in each box.

0·03   0·12   0·18   0·25

9 Fill in the spaces.

a 0·38 = $\underline{3}$ tenths 8 hundredths

b 2·71 = 2 ones 7 tenths $\underline{1}$ hundredth

c 5·09 = 5 ones $\underline{9}$ hundredths

d 8·86 = 8 ones 8 tenths $\underline{6}$ hundredths

10 6·13 can be written as $6 + \frac{1}{10} + \frac{3}{100}$. Fill in the boxes in the same way.

a $5·24 = \boxed{5} + \boxed{\frac{2}{10}} + \boxed{\frac{4}{100}}$

b $8·96 = \boxed{8} + \boxed{\frac{9}{10}} + \boxed{\frac{6}{100}}$

---

3 Write as a decimal.

a 9 hundredths = $\underline{0·09}$ b 23 hundredths = $\underline{0·23}$

c 61 hundredths = $\underline{0·61}$ d 90 hundredths = $\underline{0·9}$

4 Write as a decimal.

a $\frac{5}{100} = \underline{0·05}$ b $\frac{19}{100} = \underline{0·19}$

c $\frac{83}{100} = \underline{0·83}$ d $\frac{70}{100} = \underline{0·7}$

5 Write as a decimal.

a $3\frac{17}{100} = \underline{3·17}$ b $18\frac{9}{100} = \underline{18·09}$

c $\frac{104}{100} = \underline{1·04}$ d $\frac{233}{100} = \underline{2·33}$

6 Write the value of each decimal in hundredths.

a 0·07 = $\underline{7}$ hundredths

b 2·31 = $\underline{231}$ hundredths

c 0·5 = $\underline{50}$ hundredths

d 1·6 = $\underline{160}$ hundredths

Practice 3 | **Understanding thousandths**

1 Write as a decimal.

a
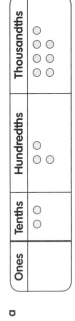

Ones	Tenths	Hundredths	Thousandths

0·237

b

Ones	Tenths	Hundredths	Thousandths

4·055

c

Ones	Tenths	Hundredths	Thousandths

6·009

d

Ones	Tenths	Hundredths	Thousandths

5·21

---

11 7·45 can be written as 7 + 0·4 + 0·05. Fill in the boxes in the same way.

a 4·31 = 4 + 0·3 + 0·01

b 9·57 = 9 + 0·5 + 0·07

12 Fill in the spaces.

a In 0·38, the digit 8 is in the __hundredths__ place.

b In 12·67, the digit in the tenths place is __6__.

c In 3·45, the digit 5 stands for __0·05__.

d In 5·02, the value of the digit 2 is __2__ hundredths.

13 Write each amount of money as a decimal.

a 40 pence = £ __0·40__

b 75 pence = £ __0·75__

c 5 pence = £ __0·05__

d 130 pence = £ __1·30__

e 10 pounds 25 pence = £ __10·25__

f 28 pounds = £ __28·00__

g 1 pound 9 pence = £ __1·09__

2 Write as a decimal.

a 7 thousandths = 0·007

b 19 thousandths = 0·019

c 235 thousandths = 0·235

d 300 thousandths = 0·3

3 Write as a decimal.

a $\frac{13}{1000}$ = 0·013

b $\frac{55}{1000}$ = 0·055

c $\frac{128}{1000}$ = 0·128

d $\frac{430}{1000}$ = 0·43

4 Write as a decimal.

a $2\frac{3}{1000}$ = 2·003

b $6\frac{61}{1000}$ = 6·061

c $7\frac{107}{1000}$ = 7·107

d $8\frac{240}{1000}$ = 8·24

5 Write as a decimal.

a $\frac{1005}{1000}$ = 1·005

b $\frac{1013}{1000}$ = 1·013

c $\frac{2341}{1000}$ = 2·341

d $\frac{3450}{1000}$ = 3·45

6 Write the value of each decimal in thousandths.

a 0·014 = 14 thousandths

b 0·178 = 178 thousandths

c 0·76 = 760 thousandths

d 1·035 = 1035 thousandths

7 Use a cross (X) to show where each decimal is on the number line.

a 0·006   **b** 0·015   **c** 0·024   **d** 0·033

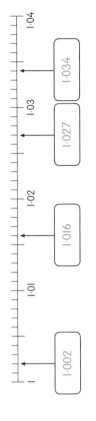

8 Write the correct decimal in each box.

1·002   1·016   1·027   1·034

9 Fill in the boxes.

a 0·126 = 1 tenth 2 hundredths [6] thousandths

b 0·352 = 3 tenths [5] hundredths 2 thousandths

51

Practice 4　Comparing decimals

1

0　0·1　0·2　0·3　0·4　0·5　0·6　0·7　0·8　0·9　1
　　　　　　a　　　c　　　d　b

Use the number line above to find the number that is:

a　0·1 more than 0·2.

b　0·3 more than 0·5.

c　0·1 less than 0·6.

d　0·2 less than 0·9.

Mark each answer with a cross (X) on the number line.

2

0·1　0·11　0·12　0·13　0·14　0·15　0·16　0·17　0·18　0·19　0·2
　　　　　　d　　　a　　　　　　c　　　　　　b

Use the number line above to find the number that is:

a　0·01 more than 0·13.

b　0·04 more than 0·16.

c　0·01 less than 0·18.

d　0·05 less than 0·17.

Mark each answer with a cross (X) on the number line.

3

0·02　0·021　0·022　0·023　0·024　0·025　0·026　0·027　0·028　0·029　0·03
　d　　　　　　　　　a　　　　　　　　b　　　　　　　c

Use the number line above to find the number that is:

a　0·001 more than 0·023.

b　0·002 more than 0·025.

c　0·001 less than 0·03.

d　0·006 less than 0·026.

Mark each answer with a cross (X) on the number line.

10　1·234 can be written as $1 + \frac{2}{10} + \frac{3}{100} + \frac{4}{1000}$. Fill in the boxes in the same way.

a　4·153 = [4] + [$\frac{1}{10}$] + [$\frac{5}{100}$] + [$\frac{3}{1000}$]

b　8·351 = [8] + [$\frac{3}{10}$] + [$\frac{5}{100}$] + [$\frac{1}{1000}$]

11　9·876 can be written as 9 + 0·8 + 0·07 + 0·006. Fill in the boxes in the same way.

a　6·426 = [6] + [0·4] + [0·02] + [0·006]

b　3·642 = [3] + [0·6] + [0·04] + [0·002]

12　In 5·074:

a　the digit 4 is in the ___thousandths___ place.

b　the value of the digit 7 is ___0·07___.

c　the digit 0 is in the ___tenths___ place.

d　the digit 4 stands for ___0·004___.

4

Use the number line to count on in steps of 0·2, starting from 0.
Write down the number that you land on after:

a 4 steps __0·8__   b 7 steps __1·4__

c 10 steps __2__   d 18 steps __3·6__

5 Continue the number pattern. Use the number line to help you.

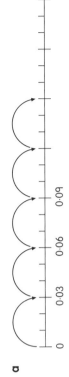

a 0·2, 0·4, 0·6, __0·8__, __1__

b 0·3, 0·5, 0·7, __0·9__, __1·1__

c 0·1, 0·4, 0·7, __1__, __1·3__

d 0·4, 0·8, 1·2, __1·6__, __2__

6

Use the number line to count back in steps of 0·3, starting from 4.
Write down the number that you land on after:

a 3 steps __3·1__   b 5 steps __2·5__

c 9 steps __1·3__   d 12 steps __0·4__

---

7 Continue the number pattern.

a

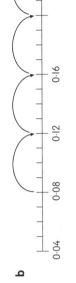

0·03, 0·06, 0·09, __0·12__, __0·15__

b

0·08, 0·12, 0·16, __0·2__, __0·24__

8

Use the number line to count back in steps of 0·04, starting from 0·4.
Write down the number that you land on after:

a 3 steps __0·28__   b 5 steps __0·2__

c 8 steps __0·08__   d 10 steps __0__

Practice 5 Comparing decimals

1 Compare the two decimals in each table. Then fill in the spaces.

a

Ones	Tenths	Hundredths
0	4	
0	3	8

0·4 is greater than 0·38 .

b

Ones	Tenths	Hundredths	Thousandths
0	0	2	
0	0	1	5

0·02 is greater than 0·015 .

c

Ones	Tenths	Hundredths	Thousandths
0	3	0	8
0	2	5	

0·25 is smaller than 0·308 .

d

Ones	Tenths	Hundredths	Thousandths
3	0	9	
3	1	9	1

3·091 is smaller than 3·19 .

---

9 Continue the number pattern.

a

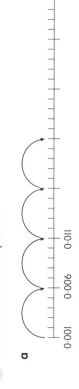

0·001 0·006 0·011

0·001, 0·006, 0·011, 0·016 , 0·021

b

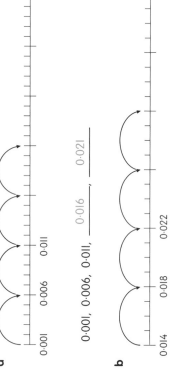

0·014 0·018 0·022

0·014, 0·018, 0·022, 0·026 , 0·03

c

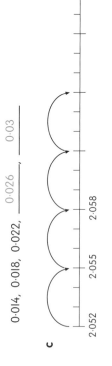

2·052 2·055 2·058

2·052, 2·055, 2·058, 2·061 , 2·064

d

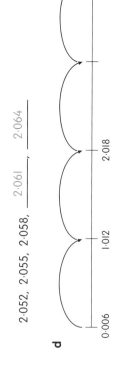
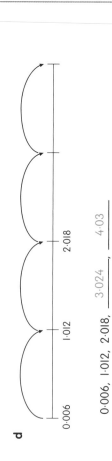

0·006 1·012 2·018

0·006, 1·012, 2·018, 3·024 , 4·03

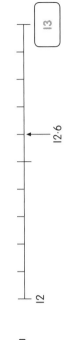

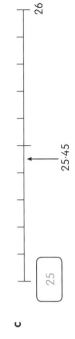

Date: _____

Practice 6 | Rounding decimals

1 Fill in the missing number in each box. Round the decimal shown to the nearest whole number.

a

12 ————↑———— 13   box: **13**
      12·6

12·6 is __13__ when rounded to the nearest whole number.

b

35 ——↑———————— 36   box: **35**
   35·3

35·3 is __35__ when rounded to the nearest whole number.

c

25 ————↑———— 26   box: **25**
        25·45

25·45 is __25__ when rounded to the nearest whole number.

d

46 —————↑—— 47   box: **46**
        46·56

46·56 is __47__ when rounded to the nearest whole number.

---

2 Which is greater?

a   1·6 or 1·8 ____1·8____
b   0·55 or 0·65 ____0·65____
c   0·07 or 0·11 ____0·11____
d   0·202 or 0·212 ____0·212____

3 Fill in the spaces with **greater than**, **smaller than** or **equal to**.

a   3·7 is ___greater than___ 0·370.
b   0·150 is ___smaller than___ 0·51.
c   0·205 is ___smaller than___ 2·05.
d   2·3 is ___equal to___ 2·30.

4 Circle the greatest decimal and underline the smallest.

a   1·03, (1·3), 0·13
b   0·5, (0·53), 0·503
c   (2·35), 2·305, 2·035
d   8·7, 8·07, (8·701)

5 Arrange the decimals in order. Begin with the smallest.

a   3·33, 3·03, 3·303   3·03, 3·303, 3·33
b   5·51, 5·051, 5·501   5·051, 5·501, 5·51
c   4, 4·01, 4·001   4, 4·001, 4·01
d   0·023, 0·203, 0·230   0·023, 0·203, 0·230

Practice 7 Rounding decimals

1 Fill in the missing decimal in each box. Round the decimal shown to the nearest tenth or 1 decimal place.

a

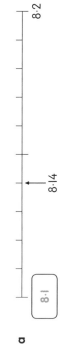

8·14

| 8·1 | | | | 8·2 |

8·14 is ___ 8·1 ___ when rounded to the nearest tenth.

b

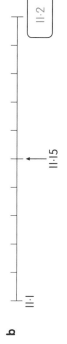

11·1   11·15

| 11·2 |

11·15 is ___ 11·2 ___ when rounded to the nearest tenth.

c

0·9   0·96

| 1·0 |

0·96 is ___ 1·0 ___ when rounded to 1 decimal place.

d

7·53

| 7·5 | | 7·6 |

7·53 is ___ 7·5 ___ when rounded to 1 decimal place.

---

2 Fill in the spaces and circles.

a

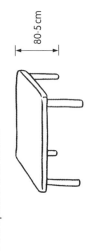

80·5 cm

Round the height of the table to the nearest centimetre.

80·5 cm ≈ 81 cm

b

£6·45

Round the cost of the shampoo to the nearest pound.

£6·45 ≈ £6

c

4·55 ℓ

Round the amount of water to the nearest litre.

4·55 ℓ ≈ 5 ℓ

d

10·3 m

Round the length of the rope to the nearest metre.

10·3 m ≈ 10 m

b

2·39   2·395   2·40

2·395 is ___2·40___ when rounded to the nearest hundredth.

c

5·99

5·994   6·00

5·994 is ___5·99___ when rounded to 2 decimal places.

4 Fill in the spaces and circles.

a The mass of a needle is 0·585 g.
Round the mass to the nearest hundredth of a gram.

0·585 g ≈ 0·59 g

b The width of a pinhead is 0·098 cm.
Round the width to 2 decimal places.

0·098 cm ≈ 0·10 cm

c 1 pint is equal to 0·568 ℓ.
Round 1 pint to the nearest hundredth of a litre.

0·568 ℓ ≈ 0·57 ℓ

---

2 Fill in the spaces and circles.

a Ravi's mass is 44·69 kg.
Round his mass to 1 decimal place.

44·69 kg ≈ 44·7 kg

b Sarah's height is 1·75 m.
Round her height to the nearest tenth of a metre.

1·75 m ≈ 1·8 m

c The distance between Jack's house and his school is 5·95 km.
Round the distance to 1 decimal place.

5·95 km ≈ 6·0 km

d 1 inch is equal to 2·54 cm.
Round 1 inch to the nearest tenth of a centimetre.

2·54 cm ≈ 2·5 cm

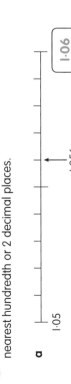

3 Fill in the missing decimal in each box. Round the decimal shown to the nearest hundredth or 2 decimal places.

a

1·05   1·056   1·06

1·056 is ___1·06___ when rounded to the nearest hundredth.

Practice 8 Fractions and decimals

1 Write each fraction as a decimal.

a $\dfrac{9}{10}$ = _0.9_

b $\dfrac{7}{10}$ = _0.7_

c $\dfrac{3}{100}$ = _0.03_

d $\dfrac{51}{100}$ = _0.51_

e $\dfrac{4}{1000}$ = _0.004_

f $\dfrac{73}{1000}$ = _0.073_

2 Write each decimal as a fraction or mixed number in its simplest form.

a $0.3 = \dfrac{3}{10}$	b $0.5 = \dfrac{5}{10}$ $= \dfrac{1}{2}$
c $0.8 = \dfrac{8}{10}$ $= \dfrac{4}{5}$	d $4.08 = 4\dfrac{8}{100}$ $= 4\dfrac{2}{25}$
e $0.25 = \dfrac{25}{100}$ $= \dfrac{1}{4}$	f $3.45 = 3\dfrac{45}{100}$ $= 3\dfrac{9}{20}$

5 Round the following decimals to the nearest whole number, tenth and hundredth.

Decimal	Rounded to the Nearest		
	Whole Number	Tenth	Hundredth
3.049	3	3.0	3.05
5.652	6	5.7	5.65
4.199	4	4.2	4.20

6 Round the following decimals to the nearest whole number, 1 decimal place and 2 decimal places.

Decimal	Rounded to		
	the Nearest Whole Number	1 Decimal Place	2 Decimal Places
21.605	22	21.6	21.61
17.954	18	18.0	17.95
55.999	56	56.0	56.00

Challenging Practice

1 a Mark 1·2 on the number line.

0   0·4   0·8   ✗   1·2

b Mark 0·12 on the number line.

0   0·03   0·06   ✗   0·12

c Mark 0·012 on the number line.

0   0·002   0·004   ✗   0·012

2 Give any number that is:

a greater than 2 but smaller than 2·1.   _Answers vary_

b greater than 1·01 but smaller than 1·02.   _Answers vary_

3 Round 3·995 to:

a the nearest whole number.   4

b the nearest tenth.   4·0

c two decimal places.   4·00

---

3 Convert each fraction to a decimal.
(Hint: Make the denominator 10 or 100.)

a $\dfrac{2}{5} = \dfrac{4}{10}$
$= 0.4$

b $\dfrac{1}{2} = \dfrac{5}{10}$
$= 0.5$

c $\dfrac{3}{2} = \dfrac{15}{10}$
$= 1.5$

d $\dfrac{5}{4} = \dfrac{125}{100}$
$= 1.25$

e $\dfrac{7}{20} = \dfrac{35}{100}$
$= 0.35$

f $\dfrac{2}{25} = \dfrac{8}{100}$
$= 0.08$

4 Write as a decimal.

a $3\dfrac{5}{100} = 3.05$

b $6\dfrac{43}{100} = 6.43$

c $4\dfrac{8}{1000} = 4.008$

d $12\dfrac{25}{1000} = 12.025$

e $8\dfrac{3}{5} = 8\dfrac{6}{10}$
$= 8.6$

f $10\dfrac{3}{20} = 10\dfrac{15}{100}$
$= 10.15$

Date: _____

Problem Solving

1 The decimals below make a pattern.
Fill in the two missing decimals.

0·01, 0·14, _0·27_ , 0·4, _0·53_ , _____, 0·66

2 The decimals below make a pattern.
Fill in the two missing decimals.

0·48, 0·39, _0·3_ , _____, 0·21, 0·12, _0·03_

34   Unit 9: Decimals (I)

Week	Learning Objectives	Thinking Skills	Resources
3	**(1) Addition** Pupils will be able to: • regroup decimals • add decimals up to 2 decimal places	• Recalling addition facts • Applying place value relationships	• Pupil Textbook 4B, pp 48 to 51 • Practice Book 4B, pp 35 to 40 • Teacher's Guide 4B, pp 64 to 67
3	**(2) Subtraction** Pupils will be able to: • regroup decimals • subtract decimals up to 2 decimal places • subtract a decimal up to 2 decimal places from a whole number	• Recalling subtraction facts • Applying place value relationships	• Pupil Textbook 4B, pp 52 to 57 • Practice Book 4B, pp 41 to 46 • Teacher's Guide 4B, pp 68 to 73
4	**(3) Word problems** Pupils will be able to solve up to two-step word problems involving addition and subtraction of decimals.	• Applying concepts of addition and subtraction • Translating verbal statements to models and/or number sentences	• Pupil Textbook 4B, pp 58 to 60 • Practice Book 4B, pp 47 to 48 • Teacher's Guide 4B, pp 74 to 76

Unit 10: Decimals (2)

Week	Learning Objectives	Thinking Skills	Resources
4	**(4) Multiplication** Pupils will be able to multiply decimals up to 2 decimal places by a 1-digit whole number.	• Recalling multiplication facts • Applying place value concepts	• Pupil Textbook 4B, pp 61 to 65 • Practice Book 4B, pp 49 to 52 • Teacher's Guide 4B, pp 77 to 81
4	**(5) Division** Pupils will be able to: • divide decimals up to 2 decimal places by a 1-digit whole number • round quotients to 1 or 2 decimal places	• Recalling division facts • Applying place value concepts • Applying rounding skills	• Pupil Textbook 4B, pp 66 to 72 • Practice Book 4B, pp 53 to 58 • Teacher's Guide 4B, pp 82 to 88
5	**(6) Estimation of decimals** Pupils will be able to estimate the answers in calculations involving addition, subtraction, multiplication and division.	• Applying rounding skills • Mental calculation	• Pupil Textbook 4B, pp 73 to 76 • Practice Book 4B, pp 59 to 62 • Teacher's Guide 4B, pp 89 to 92
5	**(7) Word problems** Pupils will be able to solve up to two-step word problems involving multiplication and division of decimals.	• Applying concepts of multiplication and division • Translating verbal statements to models and/or number sentences • Identifying relationships	• Pupil Textbook 4B, pp 77 to 79 • Practice Book 4B, pp 63 to 66 • Teacher's Guide 4B, pp 93 to 94

Week	Learning Objectives	Thinking Skills	Resources
5	*Let's Explore!* *Let's Explore!* enables pupils to find the possible combinations of 5p and 20p coins which add up to £1·15. *Maths Journal* *Maths Journal* enables pupils to use their creativity to write a word problem from given information.		• Pupil Textbook 4B, p 79 • Teacher's Guide 4B, p 95
5	*Put On Your Thinking Caps!* Pupils will be able to use the strategy of 'guess and check' to solve these questions. Review 5	• Logical reasoning Heuristic for problem solving: • Guess and check	• Pupil Textbook 4B, p 80 • Practice Book 4B, pp 67 to 68 • Teacher's Guide 4B, p 96 • Practice Book 4B, pp 69 to 78

Decimals (2)

Learning objectives: Addition

Pupils will be able to:

- regroup decimals
- add decimals up to 2 decimal places

Teaching sequence

- Introduce addition involving tenths without regrouping.
- Ask pupils to read the addition sentence and to say what it means. Encourage them to use a place value chart and counters to illustrate the addition.
- Then show them how to record the addition:
  - Write the numbers with the decimal points aligned.
  - Then add the tenths.
- Ask pupils to read the sum as: 4 tenths + 5 tenths = 9 tenths
- Emphasise that only decimals of the same place value can be added, i.e. tenths can only be added to tenths, etc. This is why we write decimals with the decimal points aligned.

- Review regrouping tenths into ones and tenths.
- Next show an addition involving tenths with regrouping.
- Encourage pupils to use a place value chart and counters to illustrate it.
- Show them how to record it:
  - Write the numbers with the decimal points aligned.
  - Then add the tenths. 6 tenths + 7 tenths = 13 tenths
  - Regroup 13 tenths as 1 one 3 tenths.
  - Write 3 in the tenths column and 1 in the ones column.
  - Add the ones. 0 ones + 0 ones + 1 one = 1 one

Key concepts

Addition of decimals can be interpreted as:

- combining two or more quantities into one
- the enlargement of a quantity, i.e. increasing the amount in the quantity
- comparison of a quantity with another, i.e. one quantity has a certain amount more than the other

What you will need

- Place value chart (see Photocopy master 3 on p 235)
- Counters

Thinking skills

- Recalling addition facts
- Applying place value relationships

Unit 10 Decimals (2)

Let's Learn!

Addition

1 Ella hopped 0·4 m from the starting line.
Ruby hopped a distance of 0·5 m.
How far did they hop altogether?
0·4 + 0·5 = ?

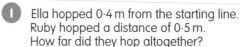

Ones	Tenths
0·4	○○○○
0·5	○○○○○
	○○○○○ ○○○○
0	9

So 0·4 + 0·5 = 0·9.
They hopped 0·9 m altogether.

Write the numbers with the decimal points aligned.

Add the **tenths**.

```
    0 · 4
+   0 · 5
---------
    0 · 9
```

4 tenths + 5 tenths = 9 tenths

2 Add 0·6 and 0·7.

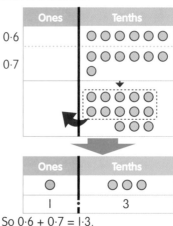

Ones	Tenths
0·6	○○○○○○
0·7	○○○○○○ ○
	○○○○○ ○○○○○ ○○○

Ones	Tenths
○	○○○
1	3

So 0·6 + 0·7 = 1·3.

Write the numbers with the decimal points aligned.

Add the **tenths**.

```
    0 · 6
+   0 · 7
---------
    1 · 3
        1
```

6 tenths + 7 tenths
= 13 tenths
= 1 one 3 tenths

48

3 Find the value of 5·4 + 7·8.

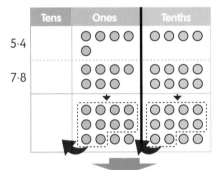

So 5·4 + 7·8 = [13·2].

Write the numbers with the decimal points aligned.

First add the **tenths**.

```
    5 · 4
  + 7 · 8
  ───────
      · 2
      ₁
```

4 tenths + 8 tenths

= [12] tenths

= [1] one [2] tenths

Then add the **ones**.

```
    5 · 4
  + 7 · 8
  ───────
  1 3 · 2
  ₁
```

5 ones + 7 ones + 1 one

= [13] ones

4 Regroup.

a 16 tenths = [1] one [6] tenths

b 3 tenths + 9 tenths = [12] tenths

= [1] one [2] tenths

5 Add.

a
```
    0 · 4
  + 0 · 2
  ───────
   [0·6]
```

b
```
    0 · 5
  + 0 · 6
  ───────
   [1·1]
```

c
```
    3 · 5
  + 2 · 9
  ───────
   [6·4]
```

6 Write in vertical form. Then add.

a 2·3 + 3·9 6·2   b 5·9 + 8 13·9   c 7·6 + 4·8 12·4

Practice Book 4B, p.35 ▶ 49

Independent work

Practice 1 in Practice Book 4B, pp 35 to 36.

Teaching sequence

3

- Demonstrate to pupils how the addition is done in the same way as in **1** and **2**.

4 to **6**

- Ask pupils to work on these questions to informally assess their understanding.

Teaching sequence

- Show pupils the procedure for the addition of hundredths without regrouping.
- Ask pupils to use place value charts and counters to illustrate the addition.
- Then show them how to record the addition:
  ○ Write the numbers with the decimal points aligned.
  ○ Then add the hundredths.
- Help pupils to read the addition as:
  2 hundredths + 7 hundredths = 9 hundredths

- Review regrouping hundredths into tenths and hundredths.
  (e.g. 14 hundredths
    = 1 tenth 4 hundredths
    = 0·14)
- Next show pupils the procedure for the addition of hundredths with regrouping.
- Ask pupils to use place value charts and counters to illustrate the addition.
- Then show them how to record the addition:

Step 1
  ○ Write the numbers with the decimal points aligned.
  ○ Then add the hundredths:
    8 hundredths + 6 hundredths = 14 hundredths
  ○ Regroup 14 hundredths as 1 tenth 4 hundredths.
  ○ Write 4 in the hundredths column and 1 as shown in the tenths column.

Step 2
  ○ Add the tenths:
    0 tenths + 2 tenths + 1 tenth = 3 tenths
  ○ Write 3 in the tenths column. Since there are no ones, a 0 is placed in the ones column.

What you will need

- Place value chart (see Photocopy master 5 on p 237)
- Counters

Independent work

Practice 2 in Practice Book 4B, pp 37 to 40.

Unit 10 Decimals (2)

7 Miya has two 1p coins. Omar has seven 1p coins. How much money do they have altogether?

Two 1p coins is £0·02.
Seven 1p coins is £0·07.
£0·02 + £0·07 = ?

	Ones	Tenths	Hundredths
0·02			○ ○
0·07			○ ○ ○ ○ ○ ○ ○
			○ ○ ○ ○ ○ ○ ○ ○ ○
	0	0	9

Write the numbers with the decimal points aligned.

Add the **hundredths**.

```
    0 · 0 2
 +  0 · 0 7
 ----------
    0 · 0 9
```

2 hundredths + 7 hundredths = 9 hundredths

So £0·02 + £0·07 = £ 0·09 .

They have £ 0·09 altogether.

8 Add 0·08 and 0·26.

	Ones	Tenths	Hundredths
0·08			○ ○ ○ ○ ○ ○ ○ ○
0·26		○ ○	○ ○ ○ ○ ○ ○
		○ ○	○ ○ ○ ○ ○ ○ ○ ○ ○ ○

	Ones	Tenths	Hundredths
		○ ○ ○	○ ○ ○ ○
	0	3	4

So 0·08 + 0·26 = 0·34.

Write the numbers with the decimal points aligned.

First add the **hundredths**.

```
    0 · 0 8
 +  0 · 2 6
 ----------
          4
          1
```

8 hundredths + 6 hundredths
= 14 hundredths
= 1 tenth 4 hundredths

Then add the **tenths**.

```
    0 · 0 8
 +  0 · 2 6
 ----------
    0 · 3 4
          1
```

0 tenths + 2 tenths + 1 tenths
= 3 tenths

50

9 Add 1·47 and 3·95.

Write the numbers in vertical form with the decimal points aligned.

First add the hundredths.	Then add the tenths.	Finally add the ones.
$\begin{array}{r} 1\cdot4\,7 \\ +\ 3\cdot9\,5 \\ \hline 2 \\ \end{array}$	$\begin{array}{r} 1\cdot4\,7 \\ +\ 3\cdot9\,5 \\ \hline 4\,2 \\ \end{array}$	$\begin{array}{r} 1\cdot4\,7 \\ +\ 3\cdot9\,5 \\ \hline 5\cdot4\,2 \\ \end{array}$
7 hundredths + 5 hundredths = 12 hundredths = 1 tenth 2 hundredths	4 tenths + 9 tenths + 1 tenth = 14 tenths = 1 one 4 tenths	1 one + 3 ones + 1 one = 5 ones

So 1·47 + 3·95 = 5·42.

10 Regroup.

a   13 hundredths = [1] tenth [3] hundredths

b   7 hundredths + 4 hundredths = [11] hundredths

=   [1] tenth [1] hundredth

11 Add.

a
$\begin{array}{r} 0\cdot0\,8 \\ +\ 0\cdot0\,4 \\ \hline \boxed{0\cdot12} \\ \end{array}$

b
$\begin{array}{r} 0\cdot1\,8 \\ +\ 0\cdot3\,9 \\ \hline \boxed{0\cdot57} \\ \end{array}$

c
$\begin{array}{r} 3\cdot4\,6 \\ +\ 0\cdot7\,6 \\ \hline \boxed{4\cdot22} \\ \end{array}$

12 Write in vertical form. Then add.

a   4·5 + 6·48
10·98

b   £10·25 + £6·35
£16·60

c   £1·99 + £1·05
£3·04

Home Maths

Encourage your child to add tenths or hundredths mentally. For example, to add 0·3 and 0·4, ask them to add 3 tenths and 4 tenths mentally to get 7 tenths or 0·7. They can also use mental calculation for subtraction.

Practice Book 4B, p.37

51

Teaching sequence

9

- Demonstrate this example in the same way as in **8**. In this example, regrouping of tenths into ones and tenths is also used in the procedure.

10 to **12**

- Ask pupils to work on these questions to informally assess their understanding.

Learning objectives: Subtraction

Pupils will be able to:

- regroup decimals
- subtract decimals up to 2 decimal places
- subtract a decimal up to 2 decimal places from a whole number

Key concepts

Subtraction of decimals can be interpreted as:

- taking away part of a quantity
- finding the missing part of a quantity given the whole and the other part
- comparison, i.e. the difference between two quantities
- complementary addition, i.e. how much must be added to a quantity to give another

Thinking skills

- Recalling subtraction facts
- Applying place value relationships

What you will need

- Place value chart (see Photocopy master 3 on p 235)
- Counters

Teaching sequence

- Introduce the subtraction of tenths without regrouping.
- Ask pupils to read the subtraction sentence and to say what it means.
- Encourage pupils to use place value charts and counters to illustrate the subtraction.
- Then show them how to record the subtraction:
  - Write the numbers with the decimal points aligned.
  - Then subtract the tenths: 5 tenths – 3 tenths = 2 tenths
  - Write 2 in the tenths column. Since there are no ones, write 0 in the ones column.
- Emphasise to pupils that, as with whole numbers, only decimals of the same place value can be subtracted, i.e. tenths can only be subtracted from tenths, hundredths from hundredths, etc. This is why we write decimals with the decimal points aligned.

- Ask pupils to work on these questions to informally assess their understanding. Note the questions are presented in columns.

Unit 10 Decimals (2)

Let's Learn!

Subtraction

1 A bottle contains $0.5\,\ell$ of water. Peter drinks $0.3\,\ell$ of water from it. How much water is left in the bottle?

$0.5 - 0.3 = ?$

Ones	Tenths
	○ ○ ⊘ ⊘ ⊘

Take away 3 tenths.

Write the numbers with the decimal points aligned.

Subtract the **tenths**.

$$\begin{array}{r} 0 \cdot 5 \\ -\ 0 \cdot 3 \\ \hline 0 \cdot 2 \end{array}$$

5 tenths – 3 tenths = 2 tenths

So $0.5 - 0.3 = 0.2$.

$0.2\,\ell$ of water is left in the bottle.

2 Subtract.

a
$$\begin{array}{r} 0 \cdot 9 \\ -\ 0 \cdot 1 \\ \hline \boxed{0.8} \end{array}$$

b
$$\begin{array}{r} 3 \cdot 5 \\ -\ 1 \cdot 4 \\ \hline \boxed{2.1} \end{array}$$

c
$$\begin{array}{r} 9 \cdot 9 \\ -\ 0 \cdot 9 \\ \hline \boxed{9.0} \end{array}$$

d
$$\begin{array}{r} 0 \cdot 8 \\ -\ 0 \cdot 5 \\ \hline \boxed{0.3} \end{array}$$

e
$$\begin{array}{r} 0 \cdot 9 \\ -\ 0 \cdot 3 \\ \hline \boxed{0.6} \end{array}$$

f
$$\begin{array}{r} 5 \cdot 8 \\ -\ 2 \cdot 1 \\ \hline \boxed{3.7} \end{array}$$

52

What you will need
- Place value chart (see Photocopy master 3 on p 235)
- Counters

3

- Ask pupils to work on these questions to informally assess their understanding. Note the questions are presented horizontally. Pupils may choose to do them mentally or write them in column format before subtracting.

4

- Review regrouping of decimals (e.g. 1 one = 10 tenths
  $1·3 = 13$ tenths
  $2·4 = 1$ one 14 tenths
  $5·7 = 4$ ones 17 tenths)
- Introduce subtraction involving tenths and ones with regrouping.
- Use a place value chart and counters to illustrate the subtraction.
- Guide pupils to see that since there are not enough tenths in 5 tenths to subtract 7 tenths, regrouping is necessary.
- Then show them how to record the subtraction:

  Step 1
  ○ Write the numbers with the decimal points aligned.
  ○ Rename 1·5 as 15 tenths. Ensure pupils understand that the value of 1·5 has not changed.

  Step 2
  ○ Subtract the tenths: 15 tenths – 7 tenths = 8 tenths
  ○ Write 8 in the tenths column. Since there are no ones, write 0 in the ones column.

5

- Ask pupils to work on these questions as a controlled practice.

Decimals (2) **Unit 10**

3 Write in vertical form. Then subtract.

a $8·9 – 7·8$ $1·1$

b $7·3 – 4$ $3·3$

c $10·7 – 2·1$ $8·6$

d $8·4 – 2·4$ $6·0$

> Remember to align the decimal points when you write in the vertical form.

4 Subtract 0·7 from 1·5.

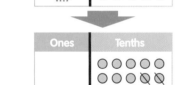

1·5

> We can't subtract 7 tenths from 5 tenths. Regroup 1 one 5 tenths.

I one 5 tenths = 15 tenths

Write the numbers with the decimal points aligned.

Subtract the **tenths**.

$$\begin{array}{r} {}^{0}\!\!\not{1}·{}^{1}5 \\ -\ 0·7 \\ \hline 0·8 \end{array}$$

15 tenths – 7 tenths = 8 tenths

> Regroup: I one 5 tenths = 15 tenths

> Take away 7 tenths.

So 1·5 – 0·7 = 0·8.

5 Regroup.

a $1 = \boxed{10}$ tenths

b $2·5 = \boxed{25}$ tenths

c $6 = 5$ ones $\boxed{10}$ tenths

d $1·6 = \boxed{16}$ tenths

e $8·7 = 7$ ones $\boxed{17}$ tenths

f $2·4 = 1$ one $\boxed{14}$ tenths

53

Teaching sequence

6 and **7**

- Ask pupils to work on these questions to informally assess their understanding.

8

- Show this example of subtraction of a 1-place decimal from a whole number.
- Guide pupils to see that the digits are aligned according to their place values. To do so, we put in a decimal point and write a zero as a placeholder, i.e. we write 2 as 2·0.
- Then show them how to record the subtraction:
  - Write the numbers with the decimal points aligned.
  - Regroup 2 ones as 1 one 10 tenths.
  - Then subtract the tenths: 10 tenths – 8 tenths = 2 tenths
  - Write 2 in the tenths column.
  - Finally subtract the ones: 1 one – 0 ones = 1 one Write 1 in the ones column.

Unit 10 Decimals (2)

6 Subtract.

a
```
    1 · 0
  - 0 · 4
    ─────
    0·6
```

b
```
    7 · 2
  - 0 · 5
    ─────
    6·7
```

c
```
    1 · 5
  - 0 · 8
    ─────
    0·7
```

7 Write in vertical form. Then subtract.

a   3·5 – 2·7 0·8   b   5·8 – 3·9 1·9   c   8·1 – 2·4 5·7

8 Subtract 0·8 from 2.

We can write 2 as 2·0.
Write the numbers with the decimal points aligned.
We cannot subtract 8 tenths from 0 tenths.

Regroup 2 ones.

```
  1   1
  2 · 0
- 0 · 8
───────
```

2 ones = 1 one 10 tenths

First subtract the **tenths**.

```
  1   1
  2 · 0
- 0 · 8
───────
      · 2
```

Then subtract the **ones**.

```
  1   1
  2 · 0
- 0 · 8
───────
  1 · 2
```

2·0 – 0·8 = 1·2

54

9 Write in vertical form. Then subtract.

a 6 – 3·6 2·4   b 10 – 7·4 2·6

c 8 – 2·5 5·5   d 11 – 3·2 7·8

10 Find the value of 3·24 – 1·06.

We can't subtract 6 hundredths from 4 hundredths.
Regroup 3 ones 2 tenths 4 hundredths.

3·24

3 ones 2 tenths 4 hundredths
= 3 ones 1 tenth 14 hundredths
Write the numbers with the decimal points aligned.

First subtract the **hundredths**.

```
   3 · ²2 ¹4
 – 1 · 0  6
_____
          8
```

14 hundredths – 6 hundredths
= 8 hundredths

Then subtract the **tenths**.

```
   3 · ¹2 ¹4
 – 1 · 0  6
_____
     · 1  8
```

1 tenth – 0 tenths = 1 tenth

Finally subtract the **ones**.
```
   3 · ¹2 ¹4
 – 1 · 0  6
_____
   2 · 1  8
```

3 ones – 1 one = 2 ones

So 3·24 – 1·06 = 2·18.

55

Teaching sequence

9

- Ask pupils to work on these questions to informally assess their understanding. Pupils may first write them in column format before subtracting.

10

- Show pupils the procedure for subtraction involving hundredths, tenths and ones with regrouping in the hundredths.

- Since there are not enough hundredths in 4 hundredths to subtract 6 hundredths, regroup 2 tenths 4 hundredths as 1 tenth 14 hundredths. Ensure pupils understand that the value of 3·24 has not changed.

- Then subtract the hundredths: 14 hundredths – 6 hundredths = 8 hundredths
Write 8 in the hundredths column.

- Next subtract the tenths: 1 tenth – 0 tenths = 1 tenth. Write 1 in the tenths column.

- Finally subtract the ones: 3 ones – 1 one = 2 ones Write 2 in the ones column.

Teaching sequence

11 to **13**

- Ask pupils to work on these questions to informally assess their understanding.

11 Regroup.

a 0·35 = 2 tenths ⬚15 hundredths

b 1·26 = ⬚1 one 1 tenth ⬚16 hundredths

c 8 tenths 2 hundredths = 7 tenths ⬚12 hundredths

d 5 tenths = 4 tenths ⬚10 hundredths

e 7 ones 5 tenths = 6 ones ⬚15 tenths

12 Subtract.

a 0·11 − 0·07 = 0·04 b 0·36 − 0·18 = 0·18 c 2·35 − 1·19 = 1·16

d 0·42 − 0·07 = 0·35 e 6·20 − 4·18 = 2·02 f 3·90 − 3·89 = 0·01

g 2·43 − 1·65 = 0·78 h 5·30 − 1·86 = 3·44 i 7·10 − 2·06 = 5·04

13 Write in vertical form. Then subtract.

a 3·85 − 1·69 2·16 b 16·78 − 5·9 10·88

c 24·67 − 0·79 23·88 d 9·40 − 3·87 5·53

56

Decimals (2) **Unit 10**

 Subtract 0·38 from 5·5.

We can write 5·5 as 5·50.
Write the numbers with the decimal points aligned.
We cannot subtract 8 hundredths from 0 hundredths.

Regroup 5 tenths.

$$5 . \overset{4}{5} \overset{1}{0}$$
$$-\ 0 . 3\ 8$$

5 tenths =
4 tenths 10 hundredths

First subtract the **hundredths**.

$$5 . \overset{4}{5} \overset{1}{0}$$
$$-\ 0 . 3\ 8$$
$$2$$

Then subtract the **tenths**.

$$5 . \overset{4}{5} \overset{1}{0}$$
$$-\ 0 . 3\ 8$$
$$. 1\ 2$$

Finally subtract the **ones**.

$$5 . \overset{4}{5} \overset{1}{0}$$
$$-\ 0 . 3\ 8$$
$$5 . 1\ 2$$

$5·5 - 0·38 = 5·12$

 Write in vertical form. Then subtract.

a 7·5 – 3·68 3·82   **b** 2 – 0·55 1·45

14

- Show this example of
  subtraction of a 2-place
  decimal from a 1-place
  decimal.
- Guide pupils to see that the
  digits are aligned according
  to their place values. To do
  so, we put in a zero as a
  placeholder, i.e. we write 5·5
  as 5·50.
- Regroup 5 tenths as 4 tenths
  10 hundredths. Then subtract.

15

- Ask pupils to work on these
  questions to informally assess
  their understanding.

Practice Book 4B, p.41

57

Learning objective: Word problems

Pupils will be able to solve up to two-step word problems involving addition and subtraction of decimals.

Thinking skills

- Applying concepts of addition and subtraction
- Translating verbal statements to models and/or number sentences

Key concept

Application of the concepts of addition and subtraction of decimals to solving word problems

Teaching sequence

- Demonstrate this one-step decimal word problem. Ask pupils to follow this procedure:

Step 1
Read the problem carefully. State the given information, any implied information and what is required to be found. If necessary, draw models to help pupils understand the problem.

Step 2
Think of a strategy that can be used to solve the problem.
Can I write a number sentence, draw a model, make a list, guess and check, act it out, or look for a pattern, ...?

Step 3
In this problem, a number sentence can be written.
What tells me that I have to subtract?

Step 4
Check whether the answer is reasonable. In this case, pupils can check their answers by working backwards.

- Ask pupils to work on this question as a controlled practice.

- Use the same procedure as in ① to discuss this two-step word problem.

Unit 10 Decimals (2)

Let's Learn!

Word problems

① Farha had £8·50. She spent £3·75 on a book. How much money did she have left?
£8·50 – £3·75 = £4·75

She had £4·75 left.

$$\begin{array}{r} £\,\overset{7}{8}\cdot\overset{1}{\overset{4}{5}}\overset{1}{0} \\ -\ £\,3\cdot75 \\ \hline £\,4\cdot75 \end{array}$$

② For a party, Hardeep prepared 2·75 ℓ of lemon squash and 1·26 ℓ of orange squash. How much squash did he prepare altogether?

2·75 + 1·26 = 4·01

He prepared 4·01 ℓ of squash altogether.

$$\begin{array}{r} 2\cdot75 \\ +\ 1\cdot26 \\ \hline 4\cdot01 \end{array}$$

③ Tom is 0·08 m taller than Amit. Ethan is 0·16 m shorter than Tom. If Ethan is 1·65 m tall, what is Amit's height?

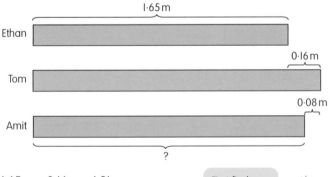

1·65 m + 0·16 m = 1·81 m

Tom's height is 1·81 m.

First find Tom's height.

1·81 m – 0·08 m = 1·73 m

Amit's height is 1·73 m.

58

4 A coat costs £66·45. A jumper costs £28·65. Ruby's dad has £75.
How much more money does he need to buy the coat and the jumper?

£ 66·45 + £ 28·65 = £ 95·10

The total cost of the coat and the jumper is £ 95·10 .

£ 95·10 − £ 75 = £ 20·10

He needs £ 20·10 more to buy the coat and the jumper.

5 A piece of material 4 m long is cut into two pieces. The first piece is
1·25 m long. How much longer is the second piece of material?

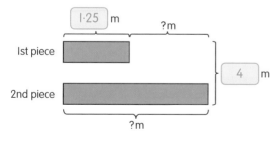

4 m − 1·25 m = 2·75 m

The length of the second piece is 2·75 m.

2·75 m − 1·25 m = 1·5 m

The second piece is 1·5 m longer than the first piece.

59

Teaching sequence

4

- Guide pupils to see that this problem involves the 'part-whole' concept of addition and the 'comparing' concept of subtraction.

5

- Guide pupils to see that this problem involves the 'part-whole' and 'comparing' concepts of subtraction.

Independent work

Practice 4 in Practice Book 4B,
pp 47 to 48.

Teaching sequence

- Guide pupils to see that this problem involves the 'part-whole' concepts of addition and subtraction.

- Guide pupils to see that this problem involves the 'comparison' and 'part-whole' concepts of addition.

Unit 10 Decimals (2)

6 Peter's mum spent £29·85 on food and £18·75 on drink. She paid the cashier £50. How much change did she get?

£ 29·85 + £ 18·75 = £ 48·60

The total cost of the food and drink is £ 48·60 .

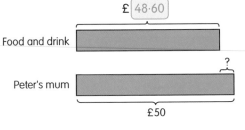

£ 50 – £ 48·60 = £ 1·40

She got £ 1·40 change.

7 Omar's dad went for a run on Monday and Tuesday. He ran 4·55 km on Monday and 1·78 km further on Tuesday than on Monday. What was the distance he ran on both days altogether?

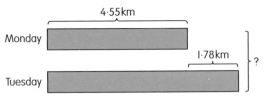

4·55 km + 1·78 km = 6·33 km

He ran 6·33 km on Tuesday.

4·55 km + 6·33 km = 10·88 km

He ran 10·88 km on both days altogether.

Practice Book 4B, p.47

60

Learning objective: Multiplication

Pupils will be able to multiply decimals up to 2 decimal places by a 1-digit whole number.

Key concepts

Multiplication of a decimal by a whole number can be interpreted as:

- repeated addition of the decimal
- comparison of one quantity with another, i.e. one quantity is *n* times as much as the other

Thinking skills

- Recalling multiplication facts
- Applying place value concepts

Let's Learn!

Multiplication

1 Look at the number line below. Starting at the point zero, Tai moves 0·2 for each step he takes. Where will Tai be on the number line after 4 steps?

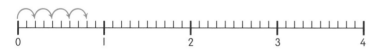

$0·2 + 0·2 + 0·2 + 0·2 = 4 × 0·2$
$4 × 2$ tenths $= 8$ tenths
$\qquad\qquad = 0·8$

After 4 steps, Tai will be at 0·8 on the number line.

2 Here is another way to multiply 0·2 by 4.

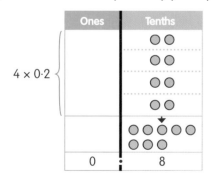

Multiply the **tenths** by 4.

$$\begin{array}{r} 0·\mathbf{2} \\ \times \qquad \mathbf{4} \\ \hline 0·\mathbf{8} \\ \hline \end{array}$$

2 tenths × 4 = 8 tenths

So $4 × 0·2 = 0·8$.

61

Teaching sequence

1 and **2**

- Introduce the multiplication of tenths by a 1-digit whole number.
- Ask pupils to read the multiplication sentence (it can be read as 4 times 2 tenths or 2 tenths multiplied by 4 to mean there are 4 groups of 2 tenths).
- Ask pupils to say what the multiplication sentence means. From the given number line or the place value chart in the textbook, guide pupils to see:
  $4 × 0·2 = 0·2 + 0·2 + 0·2 + 0·2$
  (4 groups of 2 tenths)
- Ask pupils what they think the answer is. (8 tenths)
  If necessary, help pupils to derive the answer inductively by showing these examples:
  $4 × 2$ ones $= 8$ ones
  $4 × 2$ tens $= 8$ tens
  $4 × 2$ hundreds $= 8$ hundreds
  So $4 × 2$ tenths $= 8$ tenths.
- Show pupils how the multiplication is recorded:
  ○ 4 times 2 tenths = 8 tenths
  ○ Write 8 in the tenths column. Since there are no ones, write 0 in the ones column.

What you will need
- Place value chart (see Photocopy master 3 on p 235)
- Counters

Teaching sequence

- Demonstrate a multiplication involving ones and tenths.
- Ask pupils to read the multiplication and say what it means. It can be read as 2·4 (or 2 ones 4 tenths) multiplied by 3 or 3 times 2·4 (or 2 ones 4 tenths) to mean there are 3 groups of 2 ones 4 tenths.
- Use a place value chart and counters to illustrate the multiplication.
- Then show how the multiplication is recorded:

Step 1
- Multiply 4 tenths by 3: 4 tenths × 3 = 12 tenths
- Regroup 12 tenths as 1 one 2 tenths.
  Write 2 in the tenths column and 1 in the ones column as shown.

Step 2
- Multiply 2 ones by 3: 2 ones × 3 = 6 ones
- Then add the regrouped 1 one:
  6 ones + 1 one = 7 ones
  Write 7 in the ones column.

- Ask pupils to work on these questions to informally assess their understanding.

Unit 10 Decimals (2)

3 Multiply 2·4 by 3.

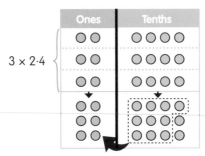

3 × 2·4

So 3 × 2·4 = 7·2.

First multiply the **tenths** by 3.

$$\begin{array}{r} 2\cdot4 \\ \times \quad 3 \\ \hline 2 \\ \hline 1 \end{array}$$

4 tenths × 3 = 12 tenths

Regroup the tenths.
12 tenths = 1 one 2 tenths

Then multiply the **ones** by 3.

$$\begin{array}{r} 2\cdot4 \\ \times \quad 3 \\ \hline 7\cdot2 \\ \hline 1 \end{array}$$

2 ones × 3 = 6 ones

Add the ones.
6 ones + 1 one = 7 ones

4 Multiply and write the product as a decimal.

a   3 tenths × 2 = [6] tenths

= [0·6]

b   6 tenths × 3 = [18] tenths

= [1] one [8] tenths

= [1·8]

Home Maths

Encourage your child to multiply tenths or hundredths mentally. For example, to multiply 0·3 by 2, ask them to multiply 3 tenths by 2 mentally to get 6 tenths or 0·6. They can also use mental calculation for division.

62

Decimals (2) Unit 10

5 Multiply.

a
$$
\begin{array}{r}
0 \cdot 2 \\
\times \quad 3 \\
\hline
\boxed{0 \cdot 6}
\end{array}
$$

b
$$
\begin{array}{r}
0 \cdot 6 \\
\times \quad 8 \\
\hline
\boxed{4 \cdot 8}
\end{array}
$$

c
$$
\begin{array}{r}
3 \cdot 7 \\
\times \quad 7 \\
\hline
\boxed{25 \cdot 9}
\end{array}
$$

6 Millie bought 3 rubbers for £0·45 each. How much did she pay altogether?

£0·45 × 3 = ?

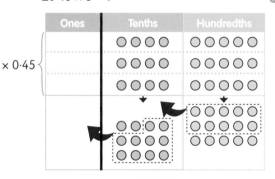

First multiply the **hundredths** by 3.

$$
\begin{array}{r}
0 \cdot 4\,5 \\
\times \quad 3 \\
\hline
5 \\
\text{\scriptsize 1}
\end{array}
$$

5 hundredths × 3
= 15 hundredths

Regroup the hundredths.
15 hundredths
= 1 tenth 5 hundredths

Then multiply the **tenths** by 3.

$$
\begin{array}{r}
0 \cdot 4\,5 \\
\times \quad 3 \\
\hline
1 \cdot 3\,5 \\
\text{\scriptsize 1}
\end{array}
$$

4 tenths × 3 = 12 tenths

Add the tenths.
12 tenths + 1 tenth
= 13 tenths

Regroup the tenths.
13 tenths = 1 one 3 tenths

Ones	Tenths	Hundredths
O	O O O	O O O O O
1	3	5

So £0·45 × 3 = £1·35.
She paid £1·35 altogether.

63

Teaching sequence

5

- Ask pupils to work on these questions to informally assess their understanding.

6

- Show pupils the procedure for a multiplication involving tenths and hundredths.
- Ask pupils to read the multiplication and say what it means. It can be read as 0·45 (45 hundredths) multiplied by 3 or 3 times 0·45 (45 hundredths) to mean there are 3 groups of 0·45 (45 hundredths).
- Use a place value chart and counters to illustrate the multiplication.
- Then show how the multiplication is recorded:

  Step 1
  - Multiply 5 hundredths by 3:
    5 hundredths × 3
    = 15 hundredths
  - Regroup 15 hundredths to 1 tenth 5 hundredths.
  - Write 5 in the hundredths column and 1 in the tenths column as shown.

  Step 2
  - Multiply 4 tenths by 3:
    4 tenths × 3 = 12 tenths
  - Then add the regrouped 1 tenth: 12 tenths + 1 tenth
    = 13 tenths
  - Regroup 13 tenths to 1 one 3 tenths.
  - Write 1 in the ones column and 3 in the tenths column.

Teaching sequence

- Demonstrate this problem using the same procedure as in 6.

 A large box of washing powder cost £15·45. Millie's dad bought 3 of these boxes. How much did he pay altogether?

£15·45 × 3 = ?

We multiply like this:

```
  1 5 · 4 5      First multiply the hundredths by 3.
×         3      5 hundredths × 3 = 15 hundredths
          5      Regroup the hundredths.
          ı      15 hundredths = 1 tenth 5 hundredths
```

```
  1 5 · 4 5      Next multiply the tenths by 3.
×         3      4 tenths × 3 = 12 tenths
      · 3 5      Add the tenths.
      ı   ı      12 tenths + 1 tenth = 13 tenths
                 Regroup the tenths.
                 13 tenths = 1 one 3 tenths
```

```
  1 5 · 4 5      Then multiply the ones by 3.
×         3      5 ones × 3 = 15 ones
    6 · 3 5      Add the ones.
    ı ı   ı      15 ones + 1 one = 16 ones
                 Regroup the ones.
                 16 ones = 1 ten 6 ones
```

```
  1 5 · 4 5      Finally multiply the tens by 3.
×         3      1 ten × 3 = 3 tens
  4 6 · 3 5      Add the tens.
  ı ı   ı        3 tens + 1 ten = 4 tens
```

So £15·45 × 3 = £46·35.

He paid £46·35 altogether.

64

Independent work

Practice 5 in Practice Book 4B,
pp 49 to 52.

8 Multiply and write the product as a decimal.

a 6 hundredths × 4 = [24] hundredths

= [2] tenths [4] hundredths

= [0·24]

b 7 hundredths × 3 = [21] hundredths

= [2] tenths [1] hundredth

= [0·21]

9 Multiply.

a
$$\begin{array}{r} 0 \cdot 0\,3 \\ \times \quad 2 \\ \hline 0·06 \end{array}$$

b
$$\begin{array}{r} 0 \cdot 0\,7 \\ \times \quad 5 \\ \hline 0·35 \end{array}$$

c
$$\begin{array}{r} 0 \cdot 6\,5 \\ \times \quad 5 \\ \hline 3·25 \end{array}$$

d
$$\begin{array}{r} 2 \cdot 0\,8 \\ \times \quad 4 \\ \hline 8·32 \end{array}$$

e
$$\begin{array}{r} 2 \cdot 1\,6 \\ \times \quad 4 \\ \hline 8·64 \end{array}$$

f
$$\begin{array}{r} 3 \cdot 1\,4 \\ \times \quad 6 \\ \hline 18·84 \end{array}$$

g
$$\begin{array}{r} 1 \cdot 0\,5 \\ \times \quad 5 \\ \hline 5·25 \end{array}$$

h
$$\begin{array}{r} 6 \cdot 9\,5 \\ \times \quad 8 \\ \hline 55·60 \end{array}$$

i
$$\begin{array}{r} 3\,1 \cdot 7\,8 \\ \times \quad 5 \\ \hline 158·90 \end{array}$$

10 Write in vertical form. Then multiply.

a £15·35 × 6   £92·10   b 26·45 m × 4   105·8 m

c 1·76 kg × 5   8·8 kg   d 18·25 m × 3   54·75 m

e 3·45 ℓ × 7   24·15 ℓ   f £17·45 × 4   £69·80

> **Practice Book 4B, p.49**

65

Teaching sequence

8 to **10**

- Ask pupils to work on these questions as controlled practices.

Learning objectives: Division

Pupils will be able to:

- divide decimals up to 2 decimal places by a I-digit whole number
- round quotients to I or 2 decimal places

Key concepts

Division of a decimal by a whole number can be interpreted as:

- sharing equally, i.e. dividing the decimal into a number of equal groups. The number of groups is determined by the divisor.
- grouping equally, i.e. dividing the set into groups of equal size. The size of each group is determined by the divisor.

Thinking skills

- Recalling division facts
- Applying place value concepts
- Applying rounding skills

Teaching sequence

- Introduce the division of a decimal (tenths) by a I-digit whole number.
- Ask pupils to read the division sentence (it is read as 8 tenths divided by 2).
- Ask pupils to say what the division sentence means (it means put 8 tenths into 2 equal groups). Illustrate the process of putting 8 tenths into 2 equal groups using the place value chart and counters.
- Ask pupils what they think the answer is (4 tenths). Help pupils to derive the answer inductively by showing these examples:
  8 ones ÷ 2 = 4 ones
  8 tens ÷ 2 = 4 tens
  8 hundreds ÷ 2 = 4 hundreds
  So 8 tenths ÷ 2 = 4 tenths
- Show pupils how the division is recorded:
  Step I
  0 ÷ 2 = 0
  Write 0 in the ones column.
  Step 2
  8 tenths ÷ 2 = 4 tenths
  Write 4 in the tenths column.

- Demonstrate this example in the same way as in ❶. Draw pupils' attention to the division of 9 hundredths by 3, which gives 3 hundredths.

Unit 10 Decimals (2)

Let's Learn!

Division

1 A ribbon that is 0·8 m long is cut into 2 equal pieces. How long is each piece?

$0.8 \div 2 = ?$

Ones	Tenths
	○ ○ ○ ○
	○ ○ ○ ○

⬇

Ones	Tenths
	○ ○ ○ ○
	○ ○ ○ ○

So 0·8 ÷ 2 = 0·4.
The length of each piece is 0·4 m.

First divide the **ones** by 2.
0 ones ÷ 2 = 0 ones

```
        0
2 ) 0 · 8
        0
```

Then divide the **tenths** by 2.
8 tenths ÷ 2 = 4 tenths

```
      0 · 4
2 ) 0 · 8
      0
      8
      8
      0
```

2 Divide 0·69 by 3.

Divide the **ones** by 3.	Divide the **tenths** by 3.	Divide the **hundredths** by 3.

```   0```
```3) 0 · 6 9```
```   0```
	``` 0 · 2```
	```3) 0 · 6 9```
	``` 0```
	``` 6```
	``` 6```
		``` 0 · 2 3```
		```3) 0 · 6 9```
		``` 0```
		``` 6```
		``` 6```
		``` 9```
		``` 9```
		``` 0```

0 ones ÷ 3 = 0 ones	6 tenths ÷ 3 = 2 tenths	9 hundredths ÷ 3 = 3 hundredths

So 69 ÷ 3 = 0·23.

66

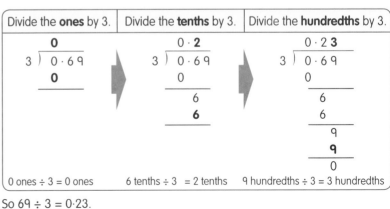

3 Divide.

a

$$2 \overline{)\ 0 \cdot 4}$$

b

$$\boxed{0 \cdot 13}$$

$$2 \overline{)\ 0 \cdot 2\,6}$$

c

$$\boxed{0 \cdot 31}$$

$$3 \overline{)\ 0 \cdot 9\,3}$$

4 Divide 0·8 by 5.

Ones	Tenths	Hundredths
	○○○○ ○○○○	

Ones	Tenths	Hundredths
	○ ○ ○ ○ ○ (○○○)	

Ones	Tenths	Hundredths
	○ ○ ○ ○ ○	○○○○○○ ○○○○○○ ○○○○○○ ○○○○○○ ○○○○○○

Ones	Tenths	Hundredths
	○ ○ ○ ○ ○	○○○○○○ ○○○○○○ ○○○○○○ ○○○○○○ ○○○○○○

So 0·8 ÷ 5 = 0·16.

First divide the **ones** by 5.
0 ones ÷ 5 = 0 ones

$$5 \overline{)\ 0 \cdot 8}$$
$$\underline{0}$$

Then divide the **tenths** by 5.
8 tenths ÷ 5 = I tenth r 3 tenths

$$5 \overline{)\ 0 \cdot 8}$$
$$\underline{0}$$
$$8$$
$$\underline{5}$$
$$3$$

Regroup the remainder 3 tenths.
3 tenths = 30 hundredths

Finally divide the remainder
30 **hundredths** by 5.
30 hundredths ÷ 5
= 6 hundredths

$$5 \overline{)\ 0 \cdot 8}$$
$$\underline{0}$$
$$8$$
$$\underline{5}$$
$$3\,0$$
$$\underline{3\,0}$$
$$0$$

67

Teaching sequence

3

- Ask pupils to work on these questions to informally assess their understanding.

4

- Demonstrate a division involving tenths in which regrouping is necessary.

- Illustrate the process of putting 8 tenths into 5 equal parts using a place value chart and counters.

- Show pupils how the division is recorded:

  Step I
  0 divided by 5 = 0
  Write 0 in the ones column.

  Step 2
  8 tenths divided by 5 = I tenth, remainder 3 tenths
  Write I in the tenths column and regroup 3 tenths to 30 hundredths.

  Step 3
  30 hundredths divided by 5 = 6 hundredths
  Write 6 in the hundredths column.

Teaching sequence

5 and **6**

- Ask pupils to work on these questions to informally assess their understanding.

7

- Show pupils the procedure for division involving ones, tenths and hundredths when regrouping is necessary.

Unit 10 Decimals (2)

5 Divide.

a   6 tenths ÷ 4 = [I] tenth r [2] tenths

b   2 tenths ÷ 4 = [20] hundredths ÷ 4

= [5] hundredths

6 Divide.

a $\overset{\boxed{0\cdot 45}}{2\,)\,\overline{0\cdot 9}}$ b $\overset{\boxed{5\cdot 5}}{5\,)\,\overline{2\,7\cdot 5}}$ c $\overset{\boxed{0\cdot 05}}{8\,)\,\overline{0\cdot 4}}$

7 A whole pizza costs £7·75. 5 children share the cost equally. How much will each pupil pay for their share?

£7·75 ÷ 5 = ?

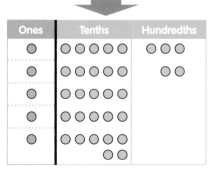

First divide the **ones** by 5.
7 ones ÷ 5 = I one r 2 ones

$$\begin{array}{r} I \\ 5\,)\,\overline{7\cdot 75} \\ \underline{5} \\ 2 \end{array}$$

Regroup the remainder 2 ones.
2 ones = 20 tenths

Add the tenths.
20 tenths + 7 tenths = 27 tenths

$$\begin{array}{r} I \\ 5\,)\,\overline{7\cdot 75} \\ \underline{5} \\ 2\,7 \end{array}$$

68

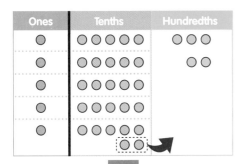

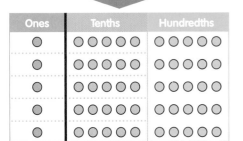

Ones	Tenths	Hundredths
○	○○○○○	○○○○○
○	○○○○○	○○○○○
○	○○○○○	○○○○○
○	○○○○○	○○○○○
○	○○○○○	○○○○○

So £7·75 ÷ 5 = £1·55.

Each pupil will pay £1·55 for their share.

Then divide the **tenths** by 5.
27 tenths ÷ 5 = 5 tenths r 2 tenths

```
        1 · 5
5 )  7 · 7 5
     5
     ─────
     2  7
     2  5
     ─────
        2
```

Regroup the remainder 2 tenths.
2 tenths = 20 hundredths

Add the hundredths.
20 hundredths + 5 hundredths
= 25 hundredths

```
        1 · 5
5 )  7 · 7 5
     5
     ─────
     2  7
     2  5
     ─────
       2 5
```

Finally divide the **hundredths** by 5.

```
        1 · 5 5
5 )  7 · 7 5
     5
     ─────
     2  7
     2  5
     ─────
        2 5
        2 5
     ─────
         0
```

69

Teaching sequence

- Ask pupils to work on these questions to informally assess their understanding.

11

- Help pupils to see that in 5 ÷ 8, since there are 0 ones in the quotient, there is still a remainder of 5 ones. To continue dividing, the 5 ones have to be regrouped into 50 tenths.
- This question requires rounding a quotient correct to the nearest tenth or 1 decimal place.
- Point out to pupils that they must first find the quotient up to 2 decimal places, before rounding it to 1 decimal place:
  - ○ 5 ÷ 8 = 0·62 (to 2 decimal places)
  - ○ Then round 0·62 to 1 decimal place.
  - ○ So 5 ÷ 8 = 0·6 correct to 1 decimal place.

Unit 10 Decimals (2)

8 Regroup into hundredths. Then divide.

    a   3 tenths 5 hundredths ÷ 7 = [35] hundredths ÷ 7

                              = [5] hundredths

                              = [0·05]

    b   4 tenths 2 hundredths ÷ 6 = [42] hundredths ÷ 6

                              = [7] hundredths

                              = [0·07]

9 Divide.

    a [0·46]   **b** [1·21]   **c** [0·75]

       2) 0·9 2   5) 6·0 5   3) 2·2 5

10 Divide.

    a £7·40 ÷ 4 £1·85   **b** £64·25 ÷ 5 £12·85 **c** £26·95 ÷ 5 £5·39

11 Find the value of 5 ÷ 8 correct to the nearest tenth or 1 decimal place.

```
        0 · 6 2
   8 )  5
        0
        5 0
        4 8
          2 0
          1 6
            4
```

    5 ones ÷ 8 = 0 ones r 5 ones

    Regroup the remainder 5 ones.
    5 ones = 50 tenths
    50 tenths ÷ 8 = 6 tenths r 2 tenths

    Regroup the remainder 2 tenths.
    2 tenths = 20 hundredths
    20 hundredths ÷ 8
    = 2 hundredths r 4 hundredths

> Divide to 2 decimal places. Then round the answer to 1 decimal place.

0·62 is 0·6 when rounded to 1 decimal place.

70 5 ÷ 8 = 0·6 correct to 1 decimal place.

12 Find the value of 13 ÷ 8 correct to the nearest hundredth or
2 decimal places.

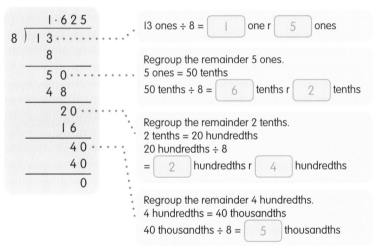

13 ones ÷ 8 = [1] one r [5] ones

Regroup the remainder 5 ones.
5 ones = 50 tenths
50 tenths ÷ 8 = [6] tenths r [2] tenths

Regroup the remainder 2 tenths.
2 tenths = 20 hundredths
20 hundredths ÷ 8
= [2] hundredths r [4] hundredths

Regroup the remainder 4 hundredths.
4 hundredths = 40 thousandths
40 thousandths ÷ 8 = [5] thousandths

Divide to 3 decimal places.
Then round the answer to
2 decimal places.

1·625 is 1·63 when rounded to 2 decimal places.

13 ÷ 8 = 1·63 correct to 2 decimal places.

13 Regroup into tenths. Then divide.

a   2 ones ÷ 3 = [20] tenths ÷ 3

= [6] tenths r [2] tenths

b   4 ones ÷ 7 = [40] tenths ÷ 7

= [5] tenths r [5] tenths

71

Teaching sequence

12

- Explain the procedure to divide
13 by 8 in the same way as in
11.

- Notice that since
1 ten ÷ 8 = 0 tens with a
remainder of 1 ten, 1 ten
3 ones is regrouped into
13 ones.

 Therefore, the first step is to
divide 13 ones by 8.

- Guide pupils to see that to
round a quotient correctly to
the nearest hundredth or
2 decimal places, they must
first find the quotient up to
3 decimal places:
  ○ 13 ÷ 8 = 1·625 (to 3 decimal
places)
  ○ Then round 1·625 to
2 decimal places.
  ○ So 13 ÷ 8 = 1·63 correct to
2 decimal places.

13

- Ask pupils to work on these
questions. These questions
require pupils to regroup ones
into tenths before dividing.

Additional activity

Encourage pupils to draw models to represent each of the following:

(a) 12·45 + 0·86

(b) 5·08 − 2·59

(c) 0·34 × 4

(d) 4·56 ÷ 6

Independent work

Practice 6 in Practice Book 4B, pp 53 to 58.

Teaching sequence

- Ask pupils to work on these questions to informally assess their understanding.

Unit 10 Decimals (2)

14 Find the value of each of the following correct to the nearest tenth or 1 decimal place.

a
$\quad \boxed{0\cdot2}$
$4\,\overline{)\,0\cdot7}$

b
$\quad \boxed{0\cdot2}$
$3\,\overline{)\,0\cdot56}$

c
$\quad \boxed{2\cdot3}$
$4\,\overline{)\quad 9}$

15 Find the value of each of the following correct to the nearest tenth or 1 decimal place.

a   0·8 ÷ 3   0·3

b   0·58 ÷ 4   0·1

c   7 ÷ 9   0·8

16 Find the value of each of the following correct to the nearest hundredth or 2 decimal places.

a
$\quad \boxed{0\cdot20}$
$4\,\overline{)\,0\cdot78}$

b
$\quad \boxed{1\cdot14}$
$7\,\overline{)\quad 8}$

c
$\quad \boxed{1\cdot67}$
$6\,\overline{)\quad 10}$

17 Find the value of each of the following correct to the nearest hundredth or 2 decimal places.

a   0·3 ÷ 7   0·04

b   0·79 ÷ 2   0·40

c   7 ÷ 6   1·17

Practice Book 4B, p.53

Let's Learn!

Estimation of decimals

1 Estimate the value of £6·75 + £15·45 by rounding the amounts
to the nearest pound.

£6·75 is £7 when rounded to the nearest pound.
£15·45 is £15 when rounded to the nearest pound.
£7 + £15 = £22
So £6·75 + £15·45 ≈ £22.

2 Estimate.

a   3·78 + 5·2 9   b   12·9 + 3·26 16   c   14·9 + 25·23 40

3 Calculate 31·65 + 8·02. Then check if your answer is reasonable
using estimation.

Calculation	Estimation
$$\begin{array}{r} 3\,1\cdot6\,5 \\ +\quad 8\cdot0\,2 \\ \hline 3\,9\cdot6\,7 \end{array}$$	31·65 ≈ 32 8·02 ≈ 8 32 + 8 = 40

How close is your
estimated answer to
the actual answer?

4 Estimate the value of 7·13 − 5·7 by rounding the numbers
to the nearest whole number.

7·13 is 7 when rounded to the nearest whole number.
5·7 is 6 when rounded to the nearest whole number.
7 − 6 = 1
So the value of 7·13 − 5·7 ≈ 1.

73

Teaching sequence

1

- Introduce estimation of
  decimals involving addition
  (e.g. £6·75 + £15·45) by
  rounding the amounts to the
  nearest pound.

- Ask pupils to round each
  decimal to the nearest whole
  number to find an estimate of
  the sum:
  - £6·75 is £7 when rounded
    to the nearest whole
    number.
  - £15·45 is £15 when
    rounded to the nearest
    whole number.
  - £7 + £15 = £22

2 and **3**

- Ask pupils to work on these
  questions as controlled
  practices on estimation of
  decimals involving addition.

4

- Show pupils the procedure
  for the estimation of decimals
  involving subtraction by first
  rounding each decimal to the
  nearest whole number, e.g.
  7·13 − 5·7 ≈ 7 − 6
  = 1

Teaching sequence

5 and **6**

- Ask pupils to work on these questions to informally assess their understanding.

- Show pupils the procedure for the estimation of decimals involving multiplication by first rounding the decimal to the nearest whole number, e.g.
$11.97 \times 2 \approx 12 \times 2$
$= 24$

- Ask pupils to work on these questions to check their understanding of estimation of decimals involving multiplication.

- Use this example to demonstrate how estimation can be used to check whether an answer is reasonable.

Unit 10 Decimals (2)

5 Estimate to find the difference.

a   9·87 – 0·96 9   b   5·75 – 5·05 1   c   24·59 – 19·68 5

6 Calculate 11·09 – 1·86. Then check if your answer is reasonable using estimation.

Calculation	Estimation
1 1 · 0 9	11·09 ≈ 11
− 1 · 8 6	1·86 ≈ 2
9 · 2 3	11 − 2 = 9

How close is your estimated answer to the actual answer?

7 Estimate the value of 11·97 × 2 by rounding 11·97 to the nearest whole number.

11·97 is 12 when rounded to the nearest whole number.
12 × 2 = 24
So the value of 11·97 × 2 ≈ 24.

8 Estimate to find the product.

a   6·02 × 8 48   b   0·98 × 13 13   c   3·15 × 9 27

9 Calculate 2·74 × 4. Then check if your answer is reasonable using estimation.

Calculation	Estimation
2 · 7 4	2·74 ≈ 3
× 4	3 × 4 = 12
1 0 · 9 6	

How close is your estimated answer to the actual answer?

10 Estimate the value of 23·64 ÷ 3.

23·64 < 21 / 24

Then divide.
24 ÷ 3 = 8
So the value of 23·64 ÷ 3 ≈ 8.

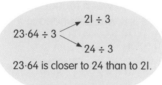

23·64 ÷ 3 < 21 ÷ 3 / 24 ÷ 3

23·64 is closer to 24 than to 21.

11 Estimate to find the quotient.

   a   12·3 ÷ 3 4   **b**   17·75 ÷ 9 2   **c**   20·99 ÷ 7 3

12 Calculate 40·4 ÷ 5. Then check if your answer is reasonable using estimation.

Calculation

```
      8 · 0 8
5 )  4 0 · 4
     4 0
     ─────
          4
          0
     ─────
        4 0
        4 0
     ─────
          0
```

Estimation

40·4 ≈ 40
40 ÷ 5 = 8

 Use estimation to check that your answer is reasonable.

13 Estimate the value of 2·49 + 6·54 by rounding the numbers to the nearest tenth or 1 decimal place.

2·49 is 2·5 when rounded to the nearest tenth.
6·54 is 6·5 when rounded to the nearest tenth.
2·5 + 6·5 = 9
So 2·49 + 6·54 ≈ 9.

75

Teaching sequence

10

- For division, the procedure is to round the dividend to a number that can be easily divided by the divisor, e.g.,
  a 23·64 ÷ 3 ≈ 24 ÷ 3 = 8
  b 4·73 ÷ 6 ≈ 4·8 ÷ 6 = 0·8
- In **a**, 23·64 is rounded to the nearest whole number, since 24 is divisible by 3.
- However in **b**, 4·73 is changed to 4·8 since 4·8 can be easily divided by 6.
- Explain to pupils that 21 is also divisible by 3. However, the value 24 is chosen because 23·64 is nearer to 24 than to 21.

11

- Ask pupils to work on this question to informally assess their understanding.

12

- Use this example to demonstrate how estimation can be used to check whether an answer is reasonable.

13

- Show pupils an example of estimation of decimals involving addition, by first rounding each decimal to the nearest tenth or 1 decimal place, e.g.
  2·49 + 6·54 ≈ 2·5 + 6·5
              = 9

Teaching sequence

Independent work
Practice 7 in Practice Book 4B,
pp 59 to 62.

- Show pupils an example of estimation of decimals involving subtraction, by first rounding each decimal to the nearest tenth or 1 decimal place, e.g.

$$10 \cdot 51 - 0 \cdot 48 \approx 10 \cdot 5 - 0 \cdot 5$$
$$= 10$$

- Demonstrate a multiplication in which rounding to the nearest tenth (1 decimal place) is necessary for estimating the product, e.g. $0 \cdot 47 \times 4$.

- Help pupils to see that it is not possible to estimate by rounding to the nearest whole number since 0·47 rounded to the nearest whole number is 0. It has to be rounded to the nearest tenth or 1 decimal place.

$$0 \cdot 47 \times 4 \approx 0 \cdot 5 \times 4$$
$$= 2$$

- For division, the procedure is to round the dividend to a number that can be easily divided by the divisor, e.g.
  (a) $0 \cdot 79 \div 4 \approx 0 \cdot 8 \div 4 = 0 \cdot 2$
  (b) $3 \cdot 46 \div 6 \approx 3 \cdot 6 \div 6 = 0 \cdot 6$

- Explain to pupils that 0·4 can also be easily divided by 4. However, the value 0·8 is chosen because 0·79 is nearer to 0·8 than to 0·4.

- Similarly, 3 can also be easily divided by 6 but 3·6 is chosen because 3·46 is nearer to 3·6 than to 3.

15

- Ask pupils to work on these questions to informally assess their understanding.

---

14 Estimate the value of each of the following.

a 10·16 – 3·78
10·16 is 10 when rounded to the nearest whole number.
3·78 is 4 when rounded to the nearest whole number.

10 – 4 = [6]

So 10·16 – 3·78 ≈ [6].

b 0·47 × 4
0·47 is 0·5 when rounded to the nearest tenth.

0·5 × 4 = [2]

So 0·47 × 4 ≈ [2].

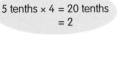
5 tenths × 4 = 20 tenths
= 2

c i 3·46 ÷ 4

$$3 \cdot 46 \div 4 \begin{cases} 3 \cdot 2 \div 4 \\ 3 \cdot 6 \div 4 \end{cases}$$

3·46 is nearer to 3·6 than to 3·2.

36 tenths ÷ 4 = 9 tenths
= 0·9

3·6 ÷ 4 = [0·9]

So 3·46 ÷ 4 ≈ [0·9].

ii 5·28 ÷ 6

$$5 \cdot 28 \div 6 \begin{cases} 4 \cdot 8 \div 6 \\ 5 \cdot 4 \div 6 \end{cases}$$

5·28 is nearer to 5·4 than to 4·8.

5·4 ÷ 6 = [0·9]

So 5·28 ÷ 6 ≈ [0·9].

15 Calculate. Then check if your answer is reasonable using estimation.

a £12·42 + £12·64   £25·06   **b** £1·45 – £0·54   £0·91

c £1·79 × 3   £5·37   **d** £1·45 ÷ 5   £0·29

 76

Practice Book 4B, p.59

Learning objective: Word problems

Pupils will be able to solve up to two-step word problems involving multiplication and division of decimals.

Key concept

Application of the concepts of multiplication and division of a decimal by a whole number to solving word problems

Thinking skills

- Applying concepts of multiplication and division
- Translating verbal statements to models and/or number sentences
- Identifying relationships

Let's Learn!

Word problems

1 A pile of 7 identical maths books is 4·55 cm high. Find the height of 9 of these books. Round your answer to 1 decimal place.

4·55 cm

?

> First find the height of 1 maths book.

$4·55 \div 7 = 0·65$

The height of 1 maths book is 0·65 cm.

$0·65 \times 9 = 5·85$

5·85 is 5·9 when rounded to 1 decimal place.

The height of 9 maths books is about 5·9 cm.

2 Miya saved £12·15. Jack saved 3 times as much money as Miya. Ella saved £24·50 less than Jack. How much money did Ella save?

£12·15

Miya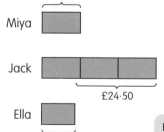

Jack

£24·50

Ella

?

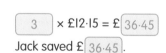 $\boxed{3} \times £12·15 = £\boxed{36·45}$

Jack saved £$\boxed{36·45}$.

$£\boxed{36·45} - £24·50 = £\boxed{11·95}$

Ella saved £$\boxed{11·95}$.

> Estimate your answer. Compare the estimate with the actual value. Is your answer reasonable?

77

Teaching sequence

1

- Use this to review the process of solving word problems.

  Step 1
  Encourage pupils to read the problem carefully. Ask pupils for the given information and what they are required to find.
  How many books are there in the pile?
  What is the total height of the 7 books?
  What do you want to find?

- Ask pupils to close their books and draw a model based on the given information. Then ask them to check their models with the one given in the textbook.

  Step 2
  Ask pupils whether any number sentences can be written.

  Step 3
  Ask pupils to write the first number sentence and explain what tells them that they have to divide. Then ask them to write the next number sentence and explain why they have to multiply.

  Step 4
  Ask pupils how they can check their answers. If necessary, remind them to work backwards to do so.

2

- Explain that this problem involves the 'comparison' concepts of multiplication and subtraction.

- Ask pupils to draw the model to illustrate these two concepts.

Independent work
Practice 8 in Practice Book 4B,
pp 63 to 66.

Teaching sequence

- Explain to pupils that this problem involves the 'repeated addition' concept of multiplication and the use of estimation.

- Guide pupils to see that this problem involves the 'part-whole' concept of subtraction and the 'sharing' concept of division.

- This activity requires pupils to write word problems given the number sentences. It enables them to apply their understanding of the concepts of multiplication and division by translating symbolic representation to verbal statements.

Unit 10 Decimals (2)

3 Mrs Thomas wants to buy 3 watches that cost £69·65 each. Estimate the least number of £5 notes she needs to buy the watches.

£69·65 ≈ £ 70

3 × £ 70 = £ 210

Total cost of 3 watches ≈ £ 210

210 ÷ 5 = 42

She needs 42 £5 notes.

4 A wooden vase and 4 identical glass vases have a total mass of 21·6 kg. The mass of the wooden vase is 3·3 kg. What is the mass of each glass vase? Round your answer to 2 decimal places.

21·6 − 3·3 = 18·3

The total mass of 4 identical glass vases is 18·3 kg.

18·3 ÷ 4 ≈ 4·58

The mass of each glass vase is 4·58 kg.

Practice Book 4B, p.63

Activity

5 a Ruby wrote these sentences.

2 × £11·20 = £22·40

£100 − £22·40 = £77·60

Write a word problem that goes with these sentences.
Answers vary

78

Objective of activities

Let's Explore! enables pupils to find the possible combinations of 5p and 20p coins which add up to £1·15.

Maths Journal enables pupils to use their creativity to write a word problem from given information.

Activity

b Omar wrote the following sentences.

> 24·15 kg − 6·45 kg = 17·7 kg
> 17·7 kg ÷ 3 = 5·9 kg

Write a word problem that goes with these sentences.
Answers vary

Let's Explore!

6 Peter has some five pence and twenty pence coins. The total amount Peter has is £1·15. How many five pence and twenty pence coins could he have?   Answers vary
Example: 5 twenty pence coins and 3 five pence coins.

Maths Journal

7 Use the information below to write one word problem. Then solve it.

Teaching sequence

6 *Let's Explore!*

- Pupils can use the strategy of making a list or table to solve this problem.

7 *Maths Journal*

- Encourage pupils to use their creativity to construct a word problem based on the toy shop advert for the sale of toy robots.

79

Objective of activity

Pupils will be able to use the strategy of 'guess and check' to solve these questions.

Thinking skill

Logical reasoning

Heuristic for problem solving

Guess and check

Independent work

Challenging Practice, Problem Solving and *Review 5* in Practice Book 4B, pp 67 to 78.

Teaching sequence

8 *Put On Your Thinking Caps!*

- Ask pupils to use the 'guess and check' strategy to solve the questions. The 'guess and check' strategy involves systematic trial and improvement. The first guess is usually not correct, but when it is checked, pupils should be able to use analytical reasoning to refine their guesses. This process should lead them to the correct answer.

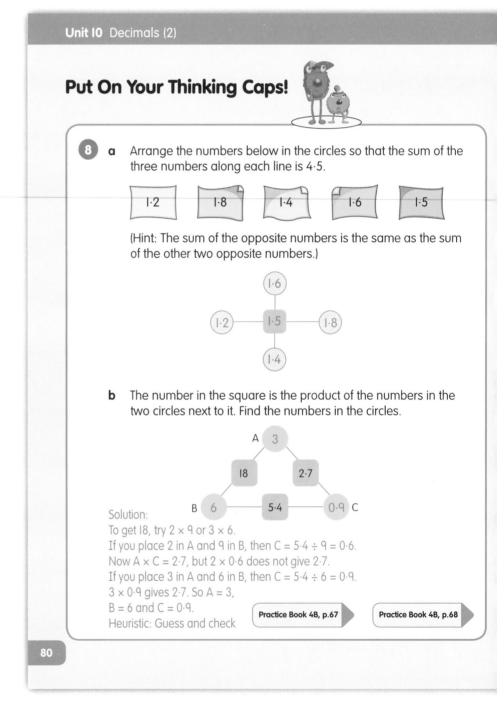

Unit 10 Decimals (2)

Put On Your Thinking Caps!

8 **a** Arrange the numbers below in the circles so that the sum of the three numbers along each line is 4·5.

| 1·2 | 1·8 | 1·4 | 1·6 | 1·5 |

(Hint: The sum of the opposite numbers is the same as the sum of the other two opposite numbers.)

1·6
1·2 — 1·5 — 1·8
1·4

b The number in the square is the product of the numbers in the two circles next to it. Find the numbers in the circles.

A 3
18   2·7
B 6 — 5·4 — 0·9 C

Solution:
To get 18, try 2 × 9 or 3 × 6.
If you place 2 in A and 9 in B, then C = 5·4 ÷ 9 = 0·6.
Now A × C = 2·7, but 2 × 0·6 does not give 2·7.
If you place 3 in A and 6 in B, then C = 5·4 ÷ 6 = 0·9.
3 × 0·9 gives 2·7. So A = 3,
B = 6 and C = 0·9.
Heuristic: Guess and check

Practice Book 4B, p.67   Practice Book 4B, p.68

80

Decimals (2)

Date: _____

Practice I   **Addition**

I   Fill in the spaces. Write the sum as a decimal.

a   0·3 + 0·5 =   3   tenths +   5   tenths

=   8   tenths

=   0·8

b   0·8 + 0·2 =   8   tenths +   2   tenths

=   10   tenths

=   1

c   0·6 + 0·7 =   6   tenths +   7   tenths

=   13   tenths

=   1·3

d   0·9 + 0·8 =   9   tenths +   8   tenths

=   17   tenths

=   1·7

2   Fill in the missing decimal to make I.

a

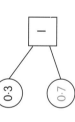

b

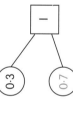

Practice 2 — Addition

1 Fill in the spaces. Write the sum as a decimal.

a $0·02 + 0·04 =$ <u>2</u> hundredths + <u>4</u> hundredths

= <u>6</u> hundredths

= <u>0·06</u>

b $0·03 + 0·07 =$ <u>3</u> hundredths + <u>7</u> hundredths

= <u>10</u> hundredths

= <u>0·1</u>

c $0·06 + 0·08 =$ <u>6</u> hundredths + <u>8</u> hundredths

= <u>14</u> hundredths

= <u>0·14</u>

d $0·09 + 0·05 =$ <u>9</u> hundredths + <u>5</u> hundredths

= <u>14</u> hundredths

= <u>0·14</u>

2 Fill in the missing decimal to make one tenth.

a 0·02, 0·08 → 0·1

b 0·06, 0·04 → 0·1

c 0·05, 0·05 → 0·1

d 0·07, 0·03 → 0·1

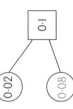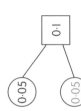

---

3 Follow the steps to add 4·8 and 3·6. Fill in the spaces.

Align the decimal points.

Step 1:
$$\begin{array}{r} 4·8 \\ + \ 3·6 \\ \hline ·4 \end{array}$$

Add the tenths.

8 tenths + 6 tenths = <u>14</u> tenths

Regroup the tenths.

<u>14</u> tenths = <u>1</u> one <u>4</u> tenths

Step 2:
$$\begin{array}{r} 4·8 \\ + \ 3·6 \\ \hline 8·4 \end{array}$$

Add the ones.

4 ones + 3 ones + <u>1</u> one = <u>8</u> ones

So $4·8 + 3·6 =$ <u>8·4</u>.

4 Add.

a
$$\begin{array}{r} 8·5 \\ + \ 2·3 \\ \hline 10·8 \end{array}$$

b
$$\begin{array}{r} 6·6 \\ + \ 1·6 \\ \hline 8·2 \end{array}$$

5 Write in vertical form. Then add.

a $15·7 + 3·8 =$ <u>19·5</u>

$$\begin{array}{r} 15·7 \\ + \ 3·8 \\ \hline 19·5 \end{array}$$

b $22·9 + 7·2 =$ <u>30·1</u>

$$\begin{array}{r} 22·9 \\ + \ 7·2 \\ \hline 30·1 \end{array}$$

4 Add.

a
```
  0·02
+ 0·35
───────
  0·37
```

b
```
  0·06
+ 0·46
───────
  0·52
```

5 Write in vertical form. Then add.

a £0·57 + £0·29 = £0·86
```
  0·57
+ 0·29
───────
  0·86
```

b 3·6 + 0·54 = 4·14
```
  3·6
+ 0·54
───────
  4·14
```

c £0·78 + £0·88 = £1·66
```
  0·78
+ 0·88
───────
  1·66
```

d 7·25 + 1·78 = 9·03
```
  7·25
+ 1·78
───────
  9·03
```

---

3 Follow the steps to add 2·34 and 0·87. Fill in the spaces.

> Align the decimal points.

Step 1:
```
  2·34
+ 0·87
───────
```

Add the hundredths.
4 hundredths + 7 hundredths
= ___ hundredths
Regroup the hundredths.
= 1 tenth 1 hundredth

Step 2:
```
  2·34
+ 0·87
───────
  ·21
```

Add the tenths.
3 tenths + 8 tenths + ___ tenth
= 12 tenths
Regroup the tenths.
12 tenths = 1 one 2 tenths

Step 3:
```
  2·34
+ 0·87
───────
  3·21
```

Add the ones.
2 ones + 0 ones + 1 one = 3 ones

So 2·34 + 0·87 = 3·21.

Practice 3 Subtraction

1 Fill in the spaces. Write the difference as a decimal.

a $0.9 - 0.4$ = 9 tenths – 4 tenths
= 5 tenths
= 0.5

b $1 - 0.3$ = 10 tenths – 3 tenths
= 7 tenths
= 0.7

c $1.3 - 0.6$ = 13 tenths – 6 tenths
= 7 tenths
= 0.7

d $1.8 - 0.9$ = 18 tenths – 9 tenths
= 9 tenths
= 0.9

---

6 Omar hops two steps on the number line. Which decimal does he land on? Write the correct decimal in each box.

a

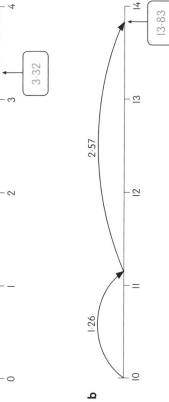

0.9   2.42

0   1   2   3   4

3.32

b

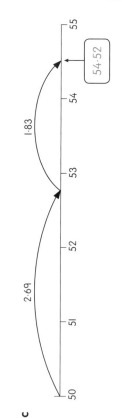

1.26   2.57

10   11   12   13   14

13.83

c

1.83   2.69

50   51   52   53   54   55

54.52

d

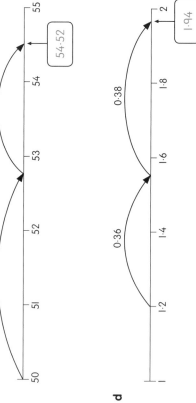

0.36   0.38

1   1.2   1.4   1.6   1.8   2

1.94

2 Follow the steps to subtract 1·7 from 3·5. Fill in the spaces.

Step 1:
$$\begin{array}{r} {}^{2}3 \cdot {}^{1}5 \\ -\ 1 \cdot 7 \\ \hline \end{array}$$

We cannot subtract 7 tenths from 5 tenths.

So we regroup 3 ones 5 tenths.

3 ones 5 tenths = __2__ ones __15__ tenths

Step 2:
$$\begin{array}{r} {}^{2}3 \cdot {}^{1}5 \\ -\ 1 \cdot 7 \\ \hline \cdot 8 \end{array}$$

Subtract the tenths.

__15__ tenths – 7 tenths = __8__ tenths

Step 3:
$$\begin{array}{r} {}^{2}3 \cdot {}^{1}5 \\ -\ 1 \cdot 7 \\ \hline 1 \cdot 8 \end{array}$$

Subtract the ones.

__2__ ones – __1__ one = __1__ one

So 3·5 – 1·7 = __1·8__ .

3 Subtract.

a
$$\begin{array}{r} 4 \cdot 6 \\ -\ 2 \cdot 2 \\ \hline 2 \cdot 4 \end{array}$$

b
$$\begin{array}{r} {}^{4}5 \cdot {}^{1}7 \\ -\ 3 \cdot 8 \\ \hline 1 \cdot 9 \end{array}$$

c
$$\begin{array}{r} {}^{6}7 \cdot {}^{1}4 \\ -\ 6 \cdot 5 \\ \hline 0 \cdot 9 \end{array}$$

4 Write in vertical form. Then subtract.

a   6·1 – 2·4
= 3·7
$$\begin{array}{r} {}^{5}6 \cdot {}^{1}1 \\ -\ 2 \cdot 4 \\ \hline 3 \cdot 7 \end{array}$$

b   3 – 1·3
= 1·7
$$\begin{array}{r} {}^{2}3 \cdot {}^{1}0 \\ -\ 1 \cdot 3 \\ \hline 1 \cdot 7 \end{array}$$

c   10·8 – 7·9
= 2·9
$$\begin{array}{r} {}^{9}10 \cdot {}^{1}8 \\ -\ 7 \cdot 9 \\ \hline 2 \cdot 9 \end{array}$$

5 Fill in the spaces. Write the difference as a decimal.

a   0·08 – 0·02   =   __8__ hundredths – __2__ hundredths
=   __6__ hundredths
=   __0·06__

b   0·15 – 0·07   =   __15__ hundredths – __7__ hundredths
=   __8__ hundredths
=   __0·08__

c   0·23 – 0·19   =   __23__ hundredths – __19__ hundredths
=   __4__ hundredths
=   __0·04__

d   0·1 – 0·06   =   __10__ hundredths – __6__ hundredths
=   __4__ hundredths
=   __0·04__

6 Follow the steps to subtract 1·54 from 4·23. Fill in the spaces.

Step 1:
$$\begin{array}{r} 4\cdot2^{1}3 \\ -\ 1\cdot5\ 4 \\ \hline \quad\ \ 9 \end{array}$$

We cannot subtract 4 hundredths from 3 hundredths.

So we regroup 2 tenths 3 hundredths.

2 tenths 3 hundredths

= ___1___ tenth ___13___ hundredths

Subtract the hundredths.

___13___ hundredths – ___4___ hundredths

= ___9___ hundredths

Step 2:
$$\begin{array}{r} ^{3}4\cdot^{1}2\ 3 \\ -\ 1\cdot5\ 4 \\ \hline \cdot6\ 9 \end{array}$$

We cannot subtract 5 tenths from ___1___ tenth.

So we regroup 4 ones ___1___ tenth.

4 ones ___1___ tenth = ___3___ ones ___11___ tenths

Subtract the tenths.

___11___ tenths – 5 tenths = ___6___ tenths

Step 3:
$$\begin{array}{r} ^{3}4\cdot^{1}2\ 3 \\ -\ 1\cdot5\ 4 \\ \hline 2\cdot6\ 9 \end{array}$$

Subtract the ones.

___3___ ones – 1 one = ___2___ ones

So 4·23 – 1·54 = ___2·69___ .

---

7 Subtract.

a
$$\begin{array}{r} 0\cdot3\ 9 \\ -\ 0\cdot0\ 7 \\ \hline 0\cdot3\ 2 \end{array}$$

b
$$\begin{array}{r} 0\cdot^{4}5^{1}1 \\ -\ 0\cdot3\ 6 \\ \hline 0\cdot1\ 5 \end{array}$$

c
$$\begin{array}{r} ^{1}2\cdot^{1}3^{2}5 \\ -\ 0\cdot4\ 8 \\ \hline 1\cdot8\ 7 \end{array}$$

8 Write in vertical form. Then subtract.

a 5·38 – 2·73 = ___2·65___
$$\begin{array}{r} ^{4}5\cdot^{1}3\ 8 \\ -\ 2\cdot7\ 3 \\ \hline 2\cdot6\ 5 \end{array}$$

b 1·06 – 0·38 = ___0·68___
$$\begin{array}{r} ^{0}1\cdot^{9}0^{1}6 \\ -\ 0\cdot3\ 8 \\ \hline 0\cdot6\ 8 \end{array}$$

c 5·6 – 1·72 = ___3·88___
$$\begin{array}{r} ^{4}5\cdot^{1}6^{1}0 \\ -\ 1\cdot7\ 2 \\ \hline 3\cdot8\ 8 \end{array}$$

d 3 – 0·42 = ___2·58___
$$\begin{array}{r} ^{2}3\cdot^{9}0^{1}0 \\ -\ 0\cdot4\ 2 \\ \hline 2\cdot5\ 8 \end{array}$$

Practice 4   Word problems

1 1 kg of grapes costs £6·90 and 1 kg of plums costs £4·55. How much do I have to pay for 1 kg of grapes and 1 kg of plums altogether?

£6·90 + £4·55 = £11·45

I have to pay £11·45 altogether.

2 A tank contained some water. After 16·5 ℓ of water was used, 8·75 ℓ of water was left. How much water was there in the tank at first?

16·5 + 8·75 = 25·25

There was 25·25 ℓ of water in the tank at first.

3 A piece of material was 4·5 m long. 2·35 m of the material was used to make a costume. How many metres of material were left?

4·5 − 2·35 = 2·15

2·15 m of material were left.

4 Tai's mum drove from school to her house which was 8·7 km away. After driving 3·75 km, she stopped at a supermarket along the way. How much further did she have to drive before she reached her house?

8·7 − 3·75 = 4·95

She had to drive 4·95 km further.

---

9 Find the difference.

a
$$
\begin{array}{r}
1\,{}^1 2 \cdot {}^1 4\ 5 \\
-\ 1\ 0 \cdot 6\ 3 \\
\hline
1 \cdot 8\ 2
\end{array}
$$

b
$$
\begin{array}{r}
{}^0{}^9 1\,{}^0 0 \cdot {}^1 1\ 3 \\
-\ \ \ 7 \cdot 1\ 8 \\
\hline
2 \cdot 9\ 5
\end{array}
$$

c
$$
\begin{array}{r}
1\,{}^0 1 \cdot 0\ 4 \\
-\ \ \ 0 \cdot 3\ 0 \\
\hline
1\ 0 \cdot 7\ 4
\end{array}
$$

d
$$
\begin{array}{r}
{}^1 2\,{}^9 0 \cdot {}^9 0\,{}^1 0 \\
-\ 1\ 4 \cdot 5\ 6 \\
\hline
5 \cdot 4\ 4
\end{array}
$$

Practice 5   Multiplication

1 Fill in the spaces. Write the product as a decimal.

a 0.3×2 = _3_ tenths × 2
= _6_ tenths
= _0.6_

b 0.6×5 = _6_ tenths × 5
= _30_ tenths
= _3_

c 0.8×7 = _8_ tenths × 7
= _56_ tenths
= _5.6_

d 0.4×10 = _4_ tenths × 10
= _40_ tenths
= _4_

2 Fill in the spaces. Write the product as a decimal.

a 0.03×3 = _3_ hundredths × 3
= _9_ hundredths
= _0.09_

b 0.02×5 = _2_ hundredths × 5
= _10_ hundredths
= _0.1_

c 0.07×7 = _7_ hundredths × 7
= _49_ hundredths
= _0.49_

d 0.12×6 = _12_ hundredths × 6
= _72_ hundredths
= _0.72_

---

5 A book costing £12·90 is now sold at £10·95. A pen is sold at a discount of 55p. How much will you save if you buy the book and the pen?

£12·90 − £10·95 = £1·95
£1·95 + £0·55 = £2·50

You will save £2·50.

6 Anna bought a jumper for £25·90 and a pair of jeans for £19·50. She paid the cashier £50. How much change did she get?

£25·90 + £19·50 = £45·40
£50 − £45·40 = £4·60

She got £4·60 change.

7 A bucket contains 3·5 ℓ of water. Another bucket contains 1·85 ℓ less water. The water from the two buckets is poured into a fish tank. How many litres of water are there in the fish tank?

3·5 ℓ − 1·85 ℓ = 1·65 ℓ
3·5 ℓ + 1·65 ℓ = 5·15 ℓ

There are 5·15 ℓ of water in the fish tank.

5 Follow the steps to multiply 1·46 by 6. Fill in the spaces.

Step 1:
$$\begin{array}{r} 1\cdot46 \\ \times\quad 6 \\ \hline \cdot6 \\ {}_{3}\ \end{array}$$

Multiply the hundredths by 6.
6 hundredths × 6 = __36__ hundredths

Regroup the hundredths.
__36__ hundredths = __3__ tenths __6__ hundredths

Step 2:
$$\begin{array}{r} 1\cdot46 \\ \times\quad 6 \\ \hline \cdot76 \\ {}_{2\ 3}\ \end{array}$$

Multiply the tenths by 6.
4 tenths × 6 = __24__ tenths

Add the tenths.
__24__ tenths + __3__ tenths = __27__ tenths

Regroup the tenths.
__27__ tenths = __2__ ones __7__ tenths

Step 3:
$$\begin{array}{r} 1\cdot46 \\ \times\quad 6 \\ \hline 8\cdot76 \\ {}_{2\ 3}\ \end{array}$$

Multiply the ones by 6.
1 one × 6 = __6__ ones

Add the ones.
__6__ ones + __2__ ones = __8__ ones

So 1·46 × 6 = __8·76__ .

---

3 Follow the steps to multiply 2·6 by 3. Fill in the spaces.

Step 1:
$$\begin{array}{r} 2\cdot6 \\ \times\ 3 \\ \hline \cdot8 \\ {}_{1}\ \end{array}$$

Multiply the tenths by 3.
6 tenths × 3 = __18__ tenths

Regroup the tenths.
__18__ tenths = __1__ one __8__ tenths

Step 2:
$$\begin{array}{r} 2\cdot6 \\ \times\ 3 \\ \hline 7\cdot8 \\ {}_{1}\ \end{array}$$

Multiply the ones by 3.
2 ones × 3 = __6__ ones

Add the ones.
__6__ ones + __1__ one = __7__ ones

So 2·6 × 3 = __7·8__ .

4 Multiply.

a
$$\begin{array}{r} 0\cdot3 \\ \times\ 8 \\ \hline 2\cdot4 \\ {}_{2}\ \end{array}$$

b
$$\begin{array}{r} 2\cdot6 \\ \times\ 4 \\ \hline 10\cdot4 \\ {}_{2}\ \end{array}$$

c
$$\begin{array}{r} 7\cdot9 \\ \times\ 5 \\ \hline 39\cdot5 \\ {}_{4}\ \end{array}$$

d
$$\begin{array}{r} 12\cdot4 \\ \times\quad 7 \\ \hline 86\cdot8 \\ {}_{1\ 2}\ \end{array}$$

Practice 6 Division

1 Divide and write the answer as a decimal.

a $0·6 ÷ 2$ = 6 tenths ÷ 2
   = 3 tenths
   = 0·3

b $0·8 ÷ 4$ = 8 tenths ÷ 4
   = 2 tenths
   = 0·2

c $1 ÷ 5$ = 10 tenths ÷ 5
   = 2 tenths
   = 0·2

d $2·4 ÷ 6$ = 24 tenths ÷ 6
   = 4 tenths
   = 0·4

2 Fill in the spaces. Write the quotient as a decimal.

a $0·08 ÷ 2$ = 8 hundredths ÷ 2
   = 4 hundredths
   = 0·04

b $0·14 ÷ 7$ = 14 hundredths ÷ 7
   = 2 hundredths
   = 0·02

c $0·27 ÷ 9$ = 27 hundredths ÷ 9
   = 3 hundredths
   = 0·03

d $0·1 ÷ 2$ = 10 hundredths ÷ 2
   = 5 hundredths
   = 0·05

---

6 Multiply.

a
```
  1 0 · 0 7
×         5
-----------
  5 0 · 3 5
        3
```

b
```
  3 · 2 9
×       3
---------
  9 · 8 7
      2
```

c
```
  1 5 · 2 4
×         8
-----------
1 2 1 · 9 2
    4 1 3
```

d
```
  7 · 4 6
×       9
---------
6 7 · 1 4
    4 5
```

7 Ella hops equal steps on the number line. Which decimal does she land on? Write the correct decimal in each box.

a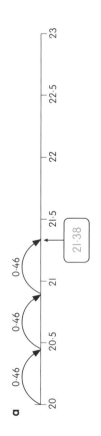

21·38

b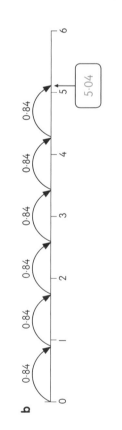

5·04

c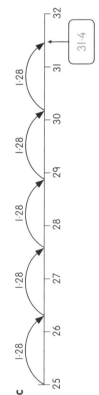

31·4

3 Follow the steps to divide 8·4 by 3. Fill in the spaces.

Step 1:
$$3\overline{)8\cdot4}$$
with 2 on top, 6 below, then 2

Divide the ones by 3.

8 ones ÷ 3 = __2__ ones r __2__ ones

Step 2:
$$3\overline{)8\cdot4}$$
2 on top, 6, then $2\ \ 4$

Regroup the remainder into tenths.

__2__ ones 4 tenths = __24__ tenths

Step 3:
$$3\overline{)8\cdot4}$$
$2\cdot8$ on top, 6, then $2\ \ 4$, $2\ \ 4$, 0

Divide the tenths by 3.

__24__ tenths ÷ 3 = __8__ tenths

So 8·4 ÷ 3 = __2·8__ .

---

4 Divide.

a
$$3\overline{)12\cdot9}$$
quotient 4·3; 12, 9, 9, 0

b
$$8\overline{)5\cdot6}$$
quotient 0·7; 0, 5 6, 5 6, 0

c
$$3\overline{)8\cdot7}$$
quotient 2·9; 6, 2 7, 2 7, 0

d
$$9\overline{)24\cdot3}$$
quotient 2·7; 18, 6 3, 6 3, 0

e
$$4\overline{)0\cdot6}$$
quotient 0·15; 0, 6, 4, 2 0, 2 0, 0

f
$$5\overline{)5\cdot2}$$
quotient 1·04; 5, 2, 0, 2 0, 2 0, 0

Answers Unit 10: Decimals (2)

5 Follow the steps to divide 5·48 by 4. Fill in the spaces.

Step 1:
$$4)\overline{5\cdot48}$$
$$\underline{4}$$
$$1$$

Divide the ones by 4.

So 5 ones ÷ 4 = __1__ one r __1__ one.

Step 2:
$$\begin{array}{r} 1\cdot3 \\ 4)\overline{5\cdot48} \\ \underline{4} \\ 14 \end{array}$$

Regroup the remainder into tenths.

__1__ one 4 tenths = __14__ tenths

Step 3:
$$\begin{array}{r} 1\cdot3 \\ 4)\overline{5\cdot48} \\ \underline{4} \\ \underline{12} \\ 2 \end{array}$$

Divide the tenths by 4.

__14__ tenths ÷ 4 = __3__ tenths r __2__ tenths

Step 4:
$$\begin{array}{r} 1\cdot3 \\ 4)\overline{5\cdot48} \\ \underline{4} \\ \underline{12} \\ 28 \end{array}$$

Regroup the remainder into hundredths.

__2__ tenths 8 hundredths = __28__ hundredths

Step 5:
$$\begin{array}{r} 1\cdot37 \\ 4)\overline{5\cdot48} \\ \underline{4} \\ \underline{12} \\ 28 \\ \underline{28} \\ 0 \end{array}$$

Divide the hundredths by 4.

__28__ hundredths ÷ 4 = __7__ hundredths

So 5·48 ÷ 4 = __1·37__ .

6 Divide.

a.
$$\begin{array}{r} 0\cdot13 \\ 4)\overline{0\cdot52} \\ 0 \\ \underline{5} \\ 4 \\ \underline{12} \\ 12 \\ 0 \end{array}$$

b.
$$\begin{array}{r} 0\cdot09 \\ 9)\overline{0\cdot81} \\ 0 \\ \underline{8} \\ 0 \\ \underline{81} \\ 81 \\ 0 \end{array}$$

c.
$$\begin{array}{r} 2\cdot02 \\ 6)\overline{12\cdot12} \\ 12 \\ \underline{1} \\ 0 \\ \underline{12} \\ 12 \\ 0 \end{array}$$

d.
$$\begin{array}{r} 1\cdot38 \\ 7)\overline{9\cdot66} \\ 7 \\ \underline{26} \\ 21 \\ \underline{56} \\ 56 \\ 0 \end{array}$$

e.
$$\begin{array}{r} 3\cdot13 \\ 5)\overline{15\cdot65} \\ 15 \\ \underline{6} \\ 5 \\ \underline{15} \\ 15 \\ 0 \end{array}$$

f.
$$\begin{array}{r} 0\cdot75 \\ 4)\overline{3} \\ 0 \\ \underline{30} \\ 28 \\ \underline{20} \\ 20 \\ 0 \end{array}$$

Practice 7 — Estimation of decimals

1. Round each number to the nearest whole number. Then estimate the sum or difference.

a $7·7 + 12·3$
   $≈ 8 + 12$
   $= 20$

b $£2·90 + £7·15$
   $≈ £3 + £7$
   $= £10$

c $£9·05 + £19·55$
   $≈ £9 + £20$
   $= £29$

d $21·8 − 11·5$
   $≈ 22 − 12$
   $= 10$

e $35·67 − 15·09$
   $≈ 36 − 15$
   $= 21$

f $£15·40 − £5·95$
   $≈ £15 − £6$
   $= £9$

---

7 Divide. Round your answer to the nearest tenth (1 decimal place).

a $7 ÷ 8 ≈ 0·9$
```
  0·87
8)7 0
  6 4
  ───
  6 0
  5 6
  ───
  4
```

b $5 ÷ 8 ≈ 0·6$
```
  0·62
8)5 0
  4 8
  ───
  2 0
  1 6
  ───
  4
```

c $11 ÷ 9 ≈ 1·2$
```
  1·22
9)1 1
  9
  ───
  2 0
  1 8
  ───
  2 0
  1 8
  ───
  2
```

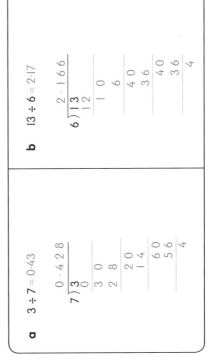

First divide to 2 decimal places. Then round your answer to 1 decimal place.

8 Divide. Round your answer to the nearest hundredth (2 decimal places).

a $3 ÷ 7 ≈ 0·43$
```
  0·428
7)3 0
  2 8
  ───
  2 0
  1 4
  ───
  6 0
  5 6
  ───
  4
```

b $13 ÷ 6 ≈ 2·17$
```
  2·166
6)1 3
  1 2
  ───
  1 0
  6
  ───
  4 0
  3 6
  ───
  4 0
  3 6
  ───
  4
```

3 Estimate the value of each of the following:

a 0·47 + 15·51
    ≈ 0·5 + 15·5
    = 16

b 9·95 − 1·46
    ≈ 10·0 − 1·5
    = 8·5

c 2·89 cm × 4
    ≈ 3 × 4
    = 12 cm

d 6·34 kg ÷ 7
    ≈ 6·3 ÷ 7
    = 0·9 kg

2 Estimate the product or quotient.

a 4·5 × 4
    ≈ 5 × 4
    = 20

b 19·6 × 3
    ≈ 20 × 3
    = 60

c 0·95 × 8
    ≈ 1 × 8
    = 8

d 24·6 ÷ 5
    ≈ 25 ÷ 5
    = 5

e 72·09 ÷ 8
    ≈ 72 ÷ 8
    = 9

f 99·75 ÷ 5
    ≈ 100 ÷ 5
    = 20

Practice 8 Word problems

1 How many litres of soup are there in 6 identical tins if each tin contains 0·33 ℓ of soup? Round your answer to the nearest litre.

$0.33 \times 6 = 1.98$
≈ 2

There are about 2 ℓ of soup in 6 identical tins.

2 A plumber cut a length of pipe into 4 equal pieces. The pipe was 0·9 m long. Find the length of each piece in metres. Round your answer to 1 decimal place.

$0.9 \div 4 = 0.225$
≈ 0.2

The length of each piece was about 0·2 m.

3 Ruby is thinking of a number. When she divides it by 7, she gets 7·35. What number is Ruby thinking of?

$7.35 \times 7 = 51.45$

Ruby is thinking of 51·45.

4 A magazine is sold for £1·95. Estimate the cost of 8 of these magazines.

$1.95 \approx 2$
$8 \times £2 = £16$

The cost of 8 magazines is about £16.

5 A piece of wood is 1·27 cm thick. Estimate the thickness of a pile of 9 of these pieces of wood.

$1.27 \approx 1$
$1 \times 9 = 9$

The thickness of a pile of 9 pieces of wood is about 9 cm.

4 2kg of runner beans cost £13·70. Find the cost of 6kg of runner beans.

£13·70 ÷ 2 = £6·85
£6·85 × 6 = £41·10

The cost of 6kg of runner beans is £41·10.

5 3 tins of soup cost £1·80. Omar bought 9 tins of soup. How much did he have to pay?

£1·80 ÷ 3 = £0·60
£0·60 × 9 = £5·40

He had to pay £5·40.

6 An artist worked for 6 days. He worked the same number of hours each day. He drew 5 small pictures an hour. In 6 days he drew 225 pictures. How many hours a day did he work?

225 ÷ 6 = 37·50 hours
37·50 ÷ 5 = 7·5 hours

He worked 7·5 hours a day.

---

7 A sack contains 10kg of potatoes. A family uses 0·85kg of potatoes a day. What mass of potatoes is left in the sack after 7 days? Give your answer to the nearest kilogram.

0·85 × 7 = 5·95
10 − 5·95 = 4·05
≈ 4

About 4kg of potatoes is left in the sack after 7 days.

8 A packet of stickers costs £1·95. What is the greatest number of packets of stickers Peter can buy with £10·00?

£1·95 ≈ £2
£10 ÷ £2 = 5

The greatest number of packets of stickers Peter can buy with £10·00 is 5.

Challenging Practice

1 3 cups and 2 bowls can hold a total of 2·88 ℓ of water. A bowl can hold 3 times as much water as a cup. Find how much water a bowl can hold.

bowl

cups

2·88 ℓ

9 units → 2·88 ℓ

1 unit → 2·88 ÷ 9 = 0·32 ℓ

3 × 0·32 = 0·96

A bowl can hold 0·96 ℓ of water.

2 James is 4·5 kg lighter than Ravi. Daniel is twice as heavy as James. The total mass of the three boys is 142·1 kg. What is James' mass?

Ravi

4·5 kg

James

Daniel

142·1 kg

4 units → 142·1 − 4·5 = 137·6 kg

1 unit → 137·6 ÷ 4 = 34·4 kg

James' mass is 34·4 kg.

Unit 10: Decimals (2)

---

9 A metal rod 9·4 m long is cut into two pieces. One piece is 3 times as long as the other. Find the length of the longer piece in metres. Round your answer to 1 decimal place.

9·4 ÷ 4 = 2·35

2·35 × 3 = 7·05

≈ 7·1

The length of the longer piece is about 7·1 m.

10 Farha bought 9 identical pencils. She gave the cashier £10·00 and was given £5·05 in change. What was the cost of 1 pencil?

£10 − £5·05 = £4·95

£4·95 ÷ 9 = £0·55

The cost of 1 pencil was £0·55.

Answers Unit 10: Decimals (2)

Problem Solving

Date: _____

1 The numbers in two circles on a line add up to the number in the square between the circles. Find the missing numbers.

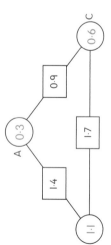

Start with the sum 0.9 since it is the smallest. Try 0.1 + 0.8.
Putting 0.1 in A and 0.8 in C will give B = 1.7 − 0.8 = 0.9, but 0.9 + 0.1 = 1, which is less than 1.4. This implies that a larger number should be put in A. Try 0.3 in A and 0.6 in C. This will give B = 1.7 − 0.6 = 1.1 and 1.1 + 0.3 is equal to 1.4. Therefore, A = 0.3, B = 1.1 and C = 0.6.

2 Miss Green bought some oranges and melons for £15·25. An orange and a melon cost £2 together and each melon costs £1·25. If she bought one more melon than oranges, how many oranges did she buy?

£15·25 − £1·25 = £14
14 ÷ 2 = 7

She bought 7 oranges.

Review 5

Date: _____

1 Write as a decimal.

a $\frac{4}{10}$ = _0.4_

b $3\frac{3}{10}$ = _3.3_

c $\frac{18}{10}$ = _1.8_

2 Give the value of each decimal in tenths.

a 0·6 = _6_ tenths

b 1·7 = _17_ tenths

c 9·5 = _95_ tenths

d 4·2 = _42_ tenths

3 Write as a decimal.

a 3 ones 4 tenths = _3·4_

b 8 ones 1 tenth = _8·1_

c 77 tenths = _7·7_

d 19 tenths = _1·9_

4 Write the correct decimal in each box.

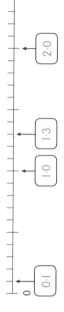

0·1 1·0 1·3 2·0 2·8

5 Fill in the boxes.

a 5·4 = 5 + $\frac{4}{10}$

b 7·1 = 7 + $\frac{1}{10}$

c 3·6 = 3 + 0·6

d 10·2 = 10 + 0·2

6 Fill in the spaces.

In 22·3, the digit 3 is in the ___tenths___ place. Its value is ___0·3___ .

7 Write as a decimal.

a $\dfrac{9}{100}$ = ___0·09___

b $2\dfrac{26}{100}$ = ___2·26___

c $\dfrac{105}{100}$ = ___1·05___

8 Give the value of each decimal in hundredths.

a 0·06 = ___6___ hundredths

b 1·33 = ___133___ hundredths

c 2·5 = ___250___ hundredths

9 Write as a decimal.

a 2 ones 6 hundredths = ___2·06___

b 5 tenths 5 hundredths = ___0·55___

c 7 ones 3 tenths 4 hundredths = ___7·34___

10 Use a cross (X) to show where each decimal is on the number line. Write the decimal below each cross.

a 0·04   b 0·15   c 0·26

11 Write as a decimal.

a 7 + 0·6 + 0·02 = ___7·62___

b 10 + 0·4 + 0·04 = ___10·44___

c $5 + \dfrac{1}{10} + \dfrac{8}{100}$ = ___5·18___

d $9 + \dfrac{3}{10} + \dfrac{7}{100}$ = ___9·37___

12 Fill in the spaces.

In 14·68, the digit 8 is in the ___hundredths___ place. Its value is ___0·08___ .

13 Fill in the spaces.

a £0·75 = ___75___ pence

b £12·25 = ___1225___ pence

c £8·05 = ___805___ pence

14 Write each amount of money as a decimal.

a 65 pence = £ ___0·65___

b 10 pounds and 90 pence = £ ___10·90___

c 2 pounds and 5 pence = £ ___2·05___

15 Write as a decimal.

a $\dfrac{9}{1000}$ = ___0·009___

b $\dfrac{63}{1000}$ = ___0·063___

c $2\dfrac{137}{1000}$ = ___2·137___

16 Give the value of each decimal in thousandths.

a 0·005 = __5__ thousandths

b 0·238 = __238__ thousandths

c 0·16 = __160__ thousandths

17 Fill in the spaces.

a 0·023 = 0 tenths 2 hundredths __3__ thousandths

b 0·407 = 4 tenths __0__ hundredths 7 thousandths

c 0·35 = __3__ tenths 5 hundredths 0 thousandths

18 1·234 can be written as $1 + \frac{2}{10} + \frac{3}{100} + \frac{4}{1000}$ or 1 + 0·2 + 0·03 + 0·004.
Fill in the boxes in the same way.

a 4·325 = 4 + $\frac{3}{10}$ + $\frac{2}{100}$ + $\frac{5}{1000}$

b 6·067 = 6 + $\frac{6}{100}$ + $\frac{7}{1000}$

c 8·104 = 8 + 0·1 + 0·004

d 10·792 = 10 + 0·7 + 0·09 + 0·002

19 Fill in the spaces.

In 12·069, the digit 9 is in the __thousandths__ place. Its value is __0·009__.

20 Fill in the spaces.

a 0·1 more than 1·1 is __1·2__.

b 0·2 less than 2 is __1·8__.

c 0·01 less than 0·1 is __0·09__.

d 0·03 more than 0·07 is __0·1__.

e 0·001 more than 0·009 is __0·01__.

f 0·002 less than 0·05 is __0·048__.

21 Use a cross (X) to show these decimals on the number line.
Write the decimal below each cross.

a 0·16   b 0·24

number line: 0   0·04   0·08   X 0·16   X 0·24

22 Fill in the spaces with **greater than** or **smaller than**.

a 4·1 is __greater than__ 0·41.

b 0·73 is __greater than__ 0·703.

c 0·126 is __smaller than__ 0·26.

23 Circle the greatest decimal and underline the smallest.

a 3·04, 3·4, 0·304

b 0·6, 0·601, 0·605

c 0·025, 0·25, 0·205

24 Give a number that is greater than 0·09 but smaller than 0·1. _Answers vary._
Examples: 0·091 to 0·099

25 Round each decimal to the nearest whole number, tenth and hundredth.

Decimal	Rounded to the Nearest		
	Whole Number	Tenth	Hundredth
8·052	8	8·1	8·05
0·607	1	0·6	0·61

26 Round 7·997 to:
a one decimal place. _8·0_
b the nearest hundredth. _8·00_

27 Ravi is 1·69 m tall. Round Ravi's height to the nearest:
a metre. _2 m_
b tenth of a metre. _1·7 m_

28 Emily's height is 1·5 m when rounded to the nearest tenth of a metre. Find, to two decimal places:
a her greatest possible height. _1·54 m_
b her shortest possible height. _1·45 m_

29 Convert each decimal to a fraction. Express your answer in the simplest form.
a $0·6 = \dfrac{3}{5}$
b $0·55 = \dfrac{11}{20}$

30 Convert each fraction to a decimal.
a $\dfrac{1}{5} =$ _0·2_
b $\dfrac{9}{20} =$ _0·45_
c $\dfrac{5}{2} =$ _2·5_
d $\dfrac{3}{4} =$ _0·75_

31 Fill in the spaces.
a 22 tenths = 2 ones _2_ tenths
b 16 hundredths = 1 tenth _6_ hundredths
c 3·2 = 3 ones _2_ tenths
d 0·45 = 4 tenths _5_ hundredths

32 Add.
a
```
  6·74
+ 2·17
------
  8·91
   1
```
b
```
  3·28
+ 0·91
------
  4·19
   1
```
c
```
  5·76
+ 4·26
------
 10·02
   1 1
```

33 Subtract.
a
```
  6 1
  7·0 5
- 1·3 3
------
  5·7 2
```
b
```
    6 1
  8·7 2
- 3·4 3
------
  5·2 9
```
c
```
  5 2 1
  6·3 6
- 5·7 9
------
  0·5 7
```

34 Multiply.
a
```
  2·5
×   5
-----
 12·5
   2
```
b
```
  5·03
×    7
-----
 35·21
    2
```
c
```
  8·46
×    6
-----
 50·76
   2 3
```

35 Divide.

a
$$6\overline{)5 \cdot 4} \quad 0 \cdot 9$$
```
    0 . 9
6 ) 5 . 4
    0
    5 4
    5 4
      0
```

b
```
    0 . 1 2
7 ) 0 . 8 4
    0
    8
    7
    1 4
    1 4
      0
```

c
```
    1 . 3 9
3 ) 4 . 1 7
    3
    1
    9
    2 7
    2 7
      0
```

d
```
    1 . 4 6
5 ) 7 . 3
    5
    2 3
    2 0
    3 0
    3 0
      0
```

36 Divide. Round your answer to 1 decimal place.

```
    0 . 1 5  ≈ 0.2
5 ) 0 . 7 7
    0
    7
    5
    2 7
    2 5
      2
```

a
```
    1 . 5 7  ≈ 1·6
4 ) 6 . 3
    4
    2 3
    2 0
    3 0
    2 8
      2
```

b
```
    0 . 8 3  ≈ 0.8
6 ) 5
    0
    5 0
    4 8
    2 0
    1 8
      2
```

c
```
    0 . 3 7  ≈ 0·4
7 ) 2 . 5 9
    0
    2 5
    2 1
    4 9
    4 9
      0
```

37 Estimate the value of each of the following:

a $49 \cdot 8 + 23 \cdot 05 \approx$ _73_

b $75 \cdot 1 - 19 \cdot 88 \approx$ _55_

c $0 \cdot 47 \times 8 \approx$ _4_

d $1 \cdot 49 \div 3 \approx$ _0·5_

38 1kg of cherries costs £9·00. Mr West buys 0·45kg of cherries. How much change will he get if he pays the cashier £10·00?

$0 \cdot 45 \times £9 = £4 \cdot 05$

$£10 - £4 \cdot 05 = £5 \cdot 95$

He will get £5·95 change.

39 A bricklayer had to build a 31·3 m long wall. After building the wall for 3 days, she still had another 5·8 m to complete. She built the same length of wall each day. How many metres did she complete in 1 day?

31·3 − 5·8 = 25·5
25·5 ÷ 3 = 8·5

She completed 8·5 m in 1 day.

40 Miya saves £4·50 each week. Her sister saves £2 more each week. When her sister has saved £14 more than Miya, how much has Miya saved?

£14 ÷ £2 = 7
£4·50 × 7 = £31·50

Miya has saved £31·50.

Review 5

78

Medium-term plan

Week	Learning Objectives	Thinking Skills	Resources
6	**(I) Seconds** Pupils will be able to: • state that 60 seconds = I minute • use seconds to measure duration • estimate duration in seconds	• Identifying relationships	• Pupil Textbook 4B, pp 81 to 85 • Practice Book 4B, pp 79 to 80 • Teacher's Guide 4B, pp 121 to 125
6	**(2) 24-hour clock** Pupils will be able to: • write the time using the 24-hour clock • convert time from the 12-hour clock to the 24-hour clock and vice versa • find the duration between two given times using the 24-hour clock • find the starting/ending time given the duration and the ending/starting time *Maths Journal* • *Maths Journal* enables pupils to make practical use of the 24-hour clock to record their daily activities • *Maths Journal* enables pupils to express their understanding of or difficulty with the concepts, skills and processes they have learnt in this topic	• Identifying relationships • Sequencing	• Pupil Textbook 4B, pp 86 to 97 • Practice Book 4B, pp 81 to 86 • Teacher's Guide 4B, pp 126 to 137
6	*Put On Your Thinking Caps!* This *Put On Your Thinking Caps!* question enables pupils to apply the strategy of using a diagram (a time line) to solve the problem.	Heuristic for problem solving: • Draw a diagram	• Pupil Textbook 4B, p 97 • Practice Book 4B, pp 87 to 88 • Teacher's Guide 4B, p 137

Summative assessment opportunities

Assessment Book 4, Test 5, pp 57 to 62
For extension, Assessment Book 4, Challenging Problems 3, p 63
Assessment Book 4, Check-up 3, pp 65 to 74

Time

Learning objectives: Seconds

Pupils will be able to:

- state that 60 seconds = 1 minute
- use seconds to measure duration
- estimate duration in seconds

Key concepts

- A second is a unit of measurement of time
- 60 seconds = 1 minute

What you will need

- Clock with a second hand
- Digital clock that shows seconds

Teaching sequence

1 and **2**

- The unit of seconds can be introduced with a clock that has a second hand, or a digital clock.

- Show pupils a clock that has a second hand. Explain to pupils that each movement of the second hand from one mark to the next on the clock face measures one second.

- Help pupils to see that it takes 5 movements of the second hand or 5 seconds for it to move from 12 to 1 (or from one number to the next) on the clock face. Ask pupils how many seconds it will take the second hand to complete one revolution of the clock face. Since there are 12 intervals between one number and the next, it will take 5 × 12 = 60 seconds.

- Tell pupils that seconds are written as 's' in short.

- Pupils should notice that when the second hand completes one revolution on the clock face, the minute hand has moved 1 minute. So 60 s = 1 min. This relationship can be seen more readily on a digital clock. As the seconds elapse from 00 to 59, the time will increase 1 minute when the seconds show 00 again.

- Tell pupils that to say "one thousand and one" takes about 1 second.

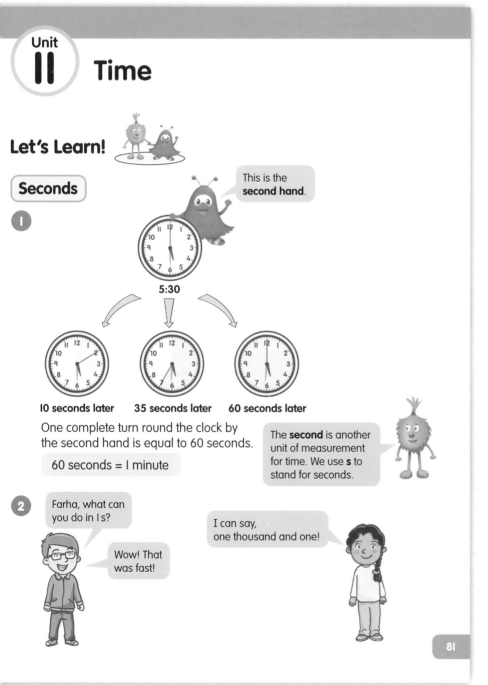

Unit 11 Time

Let's Learn!

Seconds

1

This is the **second hand**.

5:30

10 seconds later   35 seconds later   60 seconds later

One complete turn round the clock by the second hand is equal to 60 seconds.

60 seconds = 1 minute

The **second** is another unit of measurement for time. We use **s** to stand for seconds.

2

Farha, what can you do in 1 s?

Wow! That was fast!

I can say, one thousand and one!

81

What you will need
Stopwatch

Thinking skill
Identifying relationships

Teaching sequence

- This activity enables pupils to estimate the duration of I second. The duration of each activity can be compared to that of saying "one thousand and one" to roughly determine whether it takes more than, less than or about I s.

- To measure duration in seconds accurately, tell pupils that a stopwatch is used. Show pupils a stopwatch and demonstrate how it is used.

Unit II Time

Activity

3 Does each activity below take I s, more than I s or less than I s?

Activity	I s	More Than I s	Less Than I s
Say "thirty-four"			
Blink once			
Raise your hand			
Raise your hand and bring it down			
Nod twice			
Say your full name			
Say the alphabet			

4 Jack walks from one end of the classroom to the other. Ruby times him.

Jack takes 10 s to walk from one end of the classroom to the other.

What you will need
- Two containers and 30 marbles for each pair of pupils
- Stopwatch

Game

5 How to play:

Players: 2
You will need:
- 2 containers, A and B
- 30 marbles
- stopwatch

1 Player 1 puts 10 marbles into Container A.

2 Player 1 takes the marbles out of Container A one at a time and puts them into Container B as fast as they can.

3 Player 2 draws up a table as shown below. Player 2 estimates the time Player 1 will take to transfer the 10 marbles. Player 2 writes down the estimate in the table.

4 Player 2 uses a stopwatch and times Player 1 as Player 1 transfers the 10 marbles. Player 2 records the actual time taken in the table.

5 Players 1 and 2 repeat steps 1 to 4 for transferring 20 marbles and 30 marbles.

6 The players then swap roles and repeat the game.

The winner is the player whose estimates are closest to the actual times.

Player 1		
Number of Marbles Transferred	Time Taken in Seconds to Transfer Marbles	
	Estimate	Actual
10	⬭	⬭
20	⬭	⬭
30	⬭	⬭
Total Time Taken	⬭	⬭

Teaching sequence

5 *Game*

- Ask pupils to work in pairs. This game enables them to estimate duration in seconds and to check how accurate their estimates are with a stopwatch.

Teaching sequence

- Remind pupils that the time 8:20 means 20 minutes after 8 o'clock. Help pupils to understand that after 60 seconds or I minute, the time will be 2I minutes after 8 o'clock or 8:2I.
- Ask pupils what the time will be after another 60 seconds.
- Review with pupils that it takes I second for the second hand to move from one mark to the next on the clock face and 5 seconds to move from one number to the next.

- Guide pupils to find the duration in seconds on the clock faces shown in the textbook.

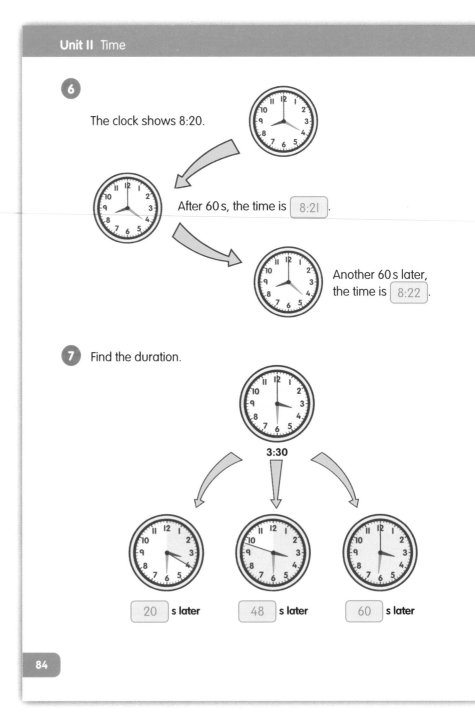

6

The clock shows 8:20.

After 60 s, the time is 8:2I .

Another 60 s later, the time is 8:22 .

7 Find the duration.

3:30

20 s later   48 s later   60 s later

84

What you will need

- Clock with a second hand
- Digital clock
- Stopwatch
- Paper
- Large clock with movable hour and minute hands (see Photocopy master 4 on p 287, Teacher's Guide IB)

Independent work

Practice I in Practice Book 4B, pp 79 to 80.

8 You will need some clock faces. Draw the missing minute and/or second hand(s) on each clock face. Then find out the time.

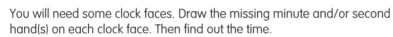
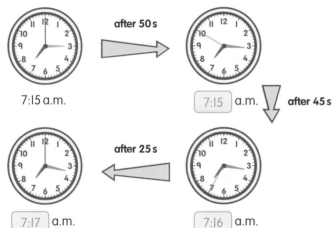

7:15 a.m.

7:15 a.m.

after 45 s

7:17 a.m.

7:16 a.m.

Activity

9 I You have 60 s to make a paper aeroplane.

2 Did you make the plane in 60 s or less?

3 Next, throw the paper aeroplane into the air and work in pairs to count the number of seconds before it falls to the ground.
One person counts using "thousands" like this: Each "thousand" stands for one second. The other uses a stopwatch.

I thousand, 2 thousand, 3 thousand, 4 thousand …

4 How many seconds did the paper aeroplane stay in the air? Compare your answers.

Practice Book 4B, p.79

85

Teaching sequence

8

- Ask pupils to write the time after 50 s as 50 seconds after 7:15 a.m. Next ask pupils how many minutes and seconds have elapsed after another 45 s. Help them to write the time in the same way.
- For the final time, ask pupils how many minutes have elapsed after another 25 s. Then ask them to write the time shown on the clock.

9

- Ask pupils to work in pairs. This activity enables pupils to measure duration in seconds by counting verbally and to then find out how accurate this method is compared to a stopwatch.

Learning objectives:
24-hour clock
Pupils will be able to:
* write the time using the 24-hour clock
* convert time from the 12-hour clock to the 24-hour clock and vice versa
* find the duration between two given times using the 24-hour clock
* find the starting/ending time given the duration and the ending/starting time

Key concepts
* Time can be expressed using the 12-hour or the 24-hour clock notation
* Duration can be measured in hours and minutes

Thinking skill
Identifying relationships

Teaching sequence

* Remind pupils how time is written using the 12-hour clock. *7:30 in the morning is written as 7:30 a.m.* Ask pupils how 7:30 in the evening is written.
* Explain to pupils that there is another way to write the time of the day: 7:30 a.m. can also be written 07:30 using the 24-hour clock.
* Guide pupils to read 07:30 as zero seven thirty hours.
* Ask pupils to give examples of different times before noon using the 12-hour clock, e.g. time school starts, time the first lesson ends, break time, and demonstrate how these times can be written using the 24-hour clock.
* Ask pupils to read each time in the 24-hour clock notation.
* Draw a time line to show pupils how the times from 1 a.m. to 11 a.m. using the 12-hour clock and the 24-hour clock are related.
* Ask pupils to read the times from 1 a.m. to 11 a.m. using the 24-hour clock.

Unit II Time

Let's Learn!

24-hour clock

 Miya gets up at the same time every day.

Look at the time on the clock.

It is 7:30 in the morning. We write it as **7:30 a.m.**
We read it as **seven thirty a.m.**

We can write the time in another way.

We can write it as **07:30**.
We read it as **zero seven thirty hours**.

> 7:30 a.m. is a way of showing time using the 12-hour clock.

> 07:30 is a way of showing time using the 24-hour clock.

86

---

2 School starts at 9:00 in the morning every day.

a Using the 12-hour clock, we write the time as [   ] . 9:00 a.m.

b Using the 24-hour clock, we write the time as [09:00].

3 Write the following times using the 24-hour clock.

a 9:15 a.m. 09:15

b 11:05 a.m. 11:05

4 Write the following times using the 12-hour clock.

a 08:45 8:45 a.m.

b 10:24 10:24 a.m.

5 School ends at 3:20 in the afternoon every day.
We write the time as 3:20 p.m.

3:20 p.m. is expressing the time using the 12-hour clock.

How do we express 3:20 p.m. using the 24-hour clock?

12 + 3 = 15

12 h   12 h

midnight   noon   3:20p.m.   midnight

00:00   12:00   15:20   00:00

12 h

3 h 20 mins

We can also say that school ends at 15:20 every day.

We read 15:20 as **fifteen twenty hours**.

Home Maths

Explain to your child that in the 24-hour clock, midnight is represented by 00:00. Using a time line, explain to your child.

To convert 1:45 p.m. to 13:45

noon   1:00 p.m.   1:45 p.m. 2:00 p.m.

12:00   13:00   13:45 14:00

1 h   45 mins

87

Teaching sequence

2

- Ask pupils to work on this question as a controlled practice.

3 and 4

- Ask pupils to work on these questions to informally assess their understanding.

5

- Tell pupils that 12 noon is written as 12:00 using the 24-hour clock, 1 p.m. is written as 13:00, 2 p.m. is written as 14:00, 3 p.m. is written as 15:00, etc. 13:00 is read as thirteen hundred hours, 14:00 is fourteen hundred hours, etc.

- Ask pupils to write the rest of the times from 4 p.m. to 11 p.m. using the 24-hour clock. Draw a time line to show pupils how the times are related.

- Guide pupils to see that to convert any time from 1 p.m. to 11 p.m. to the 24-hour clock, you can add 12 to each hour number. Inform pupils that 12 midnight is written 00:00 and is read zero hundred hours. Ask pupils to read the times from 4 p.m. to 11 p.m. in the 24-hour notation.

- Explain that 3:20 p.m. is written as 15:20 and read as fifteen twenty hours. Reinforce with some other times in the afternoon or evening, e.g. 2:30 p.m., 5:25 p.m., 8:15 p.m.

Teaching sequence

- Demonstrate another way of converting time from the 12-hour clock to the 24-hour clock. 9 p.m. is 9 hours after 12 noon. Adding 9 to 12 in this case will also give 21:00. This method will be required for finding the time when the duration from a certain time is known.

- Ask pupils to work on this question as a controlled practice.

---

6 Miya goes to bed at 9:00 every night. We write the time as 9:00 p.m.

midnight	noon	9:00 p.m. midnight
00:00	12:00	21:00 00:00

12 hours   9 hours   9 + 12 = 21

21:00 is another way of showing 9:00 p.m.
Miya goes to bed at 21:00 every night.

We read 21:00 as **twenty-one hundred hours**

7 Write the following times using the 24-hour clock.

a   8:30 p.m.   20:30

b   11:15 p.m.   23:15

a   Add 12 to 8.

b   Add 12 to 11.

 Home Maths Help your child to draw a time line for a 12-hour clock and a 24-hour clock (a guide on how to do this is given below). Then ask your child to tell the time using the time line for the 24-hour and 12-hour clocks.

24-hour clock	00:00	01:00		11:00	12:00	13:00		23:00	00:00
12-hour clock	midnight	1:00 a.m.		11:00 a.m.	noon	1:00 p.m.		11:00 p.m.	midnight

 88

Time **Unit II**

8 What is 21:35 using the 12-hour clock?

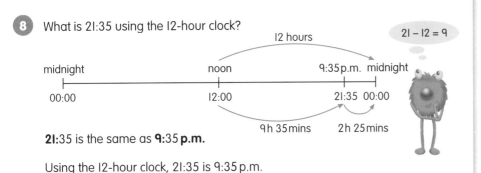

21 − 12 = 9

12 hours

midnight   noon   9:35 p.m.   midnight

00:00   12:00   21:35 00:00

9h 35 mins   2h 25 mins

21:35 is the same as **9:35 p.m.**

Using the 12-hour clock, 21:35 is 9:35 p.m.

9 Express the following times using the 24-hour clock.

a   8:50 a.m.   08:50   b   8:50 p.m.   20:50

c   6:30 a.m.   06:30   d   9:15 a.m.   09:15

e   7:40 p.m.   19:40   f   11:25 p.m.   23:25

10 Express the following times using the 12-hour clock.

a   07:35   7:35 a.m.   b   19:35   7:35 p.m.

c   08:20   8:20 a.m.   d   12:30   12:30 p.m.

e   18:40   6:40 p.m.   f   21:35   9:35 p.m.

Remember! In the 12-hour clock you must use a.m. or p.m. Why?

11 Millie started tidying her room at 16:00. She finished tidying at 16:35. How long did it take Millie to tidy her room?

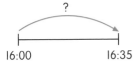

?

16:00   16:35

Draw a timeline to show the time.

Millie took 35 mins to tidy her room.

89

Teaching sequence

8

- Guide pupils to understand that to convert a time from 13:00 to 23:00 to the 12-hour clock, we subtract 12 from the hour number and write p.m. since the time is after 12 noon. So 21:35 is 9:35 p.m.

9 and **10**

- Ask pupils to work on these questions to informally assess their understanding.

11

- Introduce how to find the duration between two given times. Demonstrate how a time line can be used to find duration, e.g.

  (a) 16:00 to 18:40

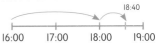

18:40

16:00   17:00   18:00   19:00

- The duration can be found by adding the duration from 16:00 to 18:00 (2 h) to that from 18:00 to 18:40 (40 mins). So the duration is 2 h + 40 mins = 2 h 40 mins.

  (b) 16:10 to 19:05

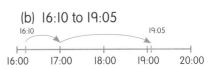

16:10   19:05

16:00   17:00   18:00   19:00   20:00

- The duration can be found by finding:
  (i) the duration from 16:10 to 17:00 (50 mins)
  (ii) the duration from 17:00 to 19:00 (2 h)
  (iii) the duration from 19:00 to 19:05 (5 mins)

  Adding them up, the duration is:
  2 h + 50 mins + 5 mins = 2 h 55 mins

- Alternatively, to find duration using the 24-hour clock, subtraction can be used. To do this in (b) above, 16:10 has to be interpreted as 16 h 10 mins after midnight and 19:05 as 19 h 5 mins after midnight. To find the duration from 16:10 to 19:05, we subtract 16 h 10 mins from 19 h 5 mins.

Unit II: Time   **129**

* Similarly, demonstrate how a time line can be used to find the ending/beginning time given the duration and the beginning/ending time, e.g.

12 25 mins after 18:00

25 mins
18:00   18:25   19:00

13 40 mins before 15:45

15:05
40 mins
15:00   15:45   16:00

14 50 mins after 19:45

50 mins
19:45   20:35
19:00   20:00   21:00

* Ask pupils how many minutes the red portion of the time line represents (45 – 40 = 5 mins). 40 mins before 15:45 is 15:05.

E.g. 35 mins before 13:15

35 mins
12:40   13:15
12:00   13:00   14:00

* 35 mins before 13:15 can be found by noting that 15 mins before 13:15 is 13:00 and 35 – 15 = 20 mins. Another 20 mins earlier will be 12:40.

* Alternatively, the ending time of an event can be found by adding the duration to the beginning time, e.g. in **14**, 19:45 is 19 h 45 mins after midnight. 50 mins later, it will be 19 h 45 mins + 50 mins = 20 h 35 mins after midnight, i.e. 20:35.

* To find the beginning time of an event, subtract the duration from the ending time, e.g. 13:15 is 13 h 15 mins after midnight. 35 mins earlier, it will be 13 h 15 mins – 35 mins = 12 h 40 mins after midnight, i.e. 12:40.

Unit II Time

12 Farha had her dinner at 18:00. She finished her dinner 25 minutes later. What time did Farha finish her dinner?

25 mins
18:00   ?

Count on.

Farha finished her dinner at 18:25.

13 Ella finished her piano lesson at 15:45. Her lesson lasted 40 minutes. What time did Ella begin her piano lesson?

40 mins
?   15:45

Count back.

Ella began her piano lesson at 15:05.

14 Ben left the cinema at 19:45. He took a bus and got home 50 minutes later. What time did Ben get home?

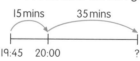

15 mins   35 mins
19:45   20:00   ?

50 ⟨ 15 / 35

Ben got home at 20:35.

15 Miya began painting a picture at 12:25. She finished painting the picture 45 minutes later. What time did Miya finish painting the picture?

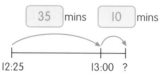

35 mins   10 mins
12:25   13:00 ?

45 ⟨ ? / ?

Miya finished painting the picture at 13:10 .

16 Peter's dad baked a cake in the oven for 50 minutes. He removed the cake from the oven at 10:15. What time did Peter's dad start baking?

50 mins = 15 mins + [35] mins

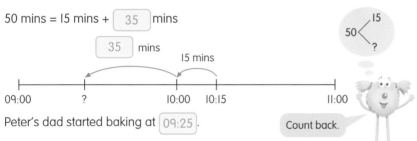

Peter's dad started baking at [09:25].

Count back.

17 A music concert started at 19:45. It ended at 21:20. How long did the music concert last?

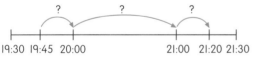

The concert lasted [1] h [35] mins.

18 Omar took 40 minutes to write a short story. He started writing at 11:45. What time did he finish writing?

He finished writing at [12:25].

19 Sophia took a train from London Paddington station and reached Heathrow Central station 26 minutes later. She arrived at Heathrow Central station at 11:20. What time did she board the train at London Paddington station?

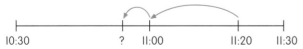

She boarded the train at [10:54].

Teaching sequence

16 to **19**

- Ask pupils to work on these questions to informally assess their understanding.

91

Teaching sequence

- Demonstrate the two possible ways of finding the ending time when the duration is more than 1 hour.
- Alternatively, the ending time can be found by addition.

- Ask pupils to work on this question as a controlled practice.

---

20 Tai's art lesson started at 15:30. The lesson lasted 1h 10 mins. What time did the art lesson end?

Method 1

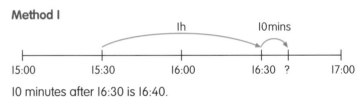

10 minutes after 16:30 is 16:40.

Method 2

1h 10 mins = 70 mins = 30 mins + 40 mins

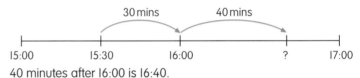

40 minutes after 16:00 is 16:40.

The art lesson ended at 16:40.

21 A film ended at 22:05. It lasted 2h 25 mins. What time did the film start?

Method 1

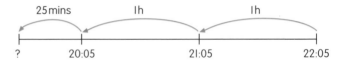

Method 2

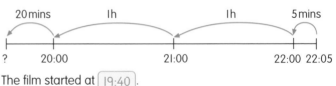

The film started at [19:40].

Home Maths — You can help your child to become more familiar with 24-hour clock times by looking at bus or train timetables together. Encourage your child to use the timetables to work out when a bus or train is due.

92

Additional activity

Provide pupils with an old television programme schedule cut out from a magazine or newspaper and ask them to write the times of the programmes using the 24-hour clock.

Teaching sequence

22

- Demonstrate how to present the three durations in a table.

23

- Ask pupils to work on this question as a controlled practice.

22 A train left Birmingham at 13:45 and arrived in London at 15:10 on the same day. How long was the journey?

Draw a timeline to show the time taken

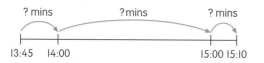

? mins   ?mins   ? mins

13:45   14:00   15:00 15:10

From	To	Time Taken
13:45	14:00	15 mins
14:00	15:00	60 mins = 1h
15:00	15:10	10 mins
	Total time	1h 25 mins

The journey was 1h 25 mins long.

23 Omar's dad started running at 17:45 and finished at 19:15. How long did he run for?

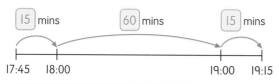

15 mins   60 mins   15 mins

17:45   18:00   19:00   19:15

From	To	Time Taken
17:45	18:00	15 mins
18:00	19:00	60 mins = 1h
19:00	19:15	15 mins
	Total time	1h 30 mins

He ran for [1] h [30] mins.

93

Teaching sequence

- This example illustrates the scenario of an event that begins on one day and ends on the next day. Ask pupils to find the duration given the starting and ending times.

 Ruby's aunt went to see a band on Saturday. The band finished playing at 23:30. Ruby's aunt got home at 00:15.

a Did she get home the same day?

b How long did it take her to get home?

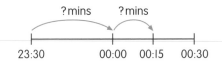

?mins   ?mins

23:30   00:00   00:15   00:30

a

Midnight is written as 00:00.
00:15 is after midnight. Ruby's aunt
got home on Sunday!

b

From	To	Time Taken
23:30	00:00 (end of Saturday)	30 mins
00:00 (beginning of Sunday)	00:15	15 mins
	Total time	45 mins

It took Ruby's aunt 45 mins to get home.

Objective of activity

Maths Journal enables pupils to make practical use of the 24-hour clock to record their daily activities.

Thinking skill

Sequencing

Teaching sequence

25

- Ask pupils to work on this question as a controlled practice.

26 *Maths Journal*

- This task enables pupils to make practical use of the 24-hour clock to write a diary of their daily activities.

25 A train left Paddington station at 22:50 on Wednesday. It arrived in Cardiff at 01:20. How long was the journey? Did the train reach Cardiff on the same day or the next day?

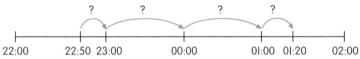

From	To	Time Taken
22:50	23:00	10 mins
23:00	00:00	1 h
00:00	01:00	1 h
01:00	01:20	20 mins

The journey was [2] h [30] mins long.

The train reached Cardiff the [next] day.

Maths Journal

26 Using the 24-hour clock, make a diary of your activities on a school day from the time you get up to the time you go to bed.

Example

07:30 :
I get up.
07:30 – 08:00 :
I get ready for school.

95

Teaching sequence

a

- This activity enables pupils to reinforce their knowledge of the 24-hour clock by constructing a word problem given a time and the duration of an event.

b

- This activity exposes pupils to a real situation regarding the departure times, arrival times and duration of train travel. The activity also serves to consolidate the processes they have learnt.

Independent work

Practice 2 in Practice Book 4B, pp 81 to 86.

Activity

27 Work in pairs.

a Use the words below to write a word problem.

20:35 began	1 h 45 mins finished	Mr Smith what time	painting he took

Exchange word problems with your partner and try to solve them.

b The table below shows the departure times of trains from London stations and their arrival times at various destinations in the UK.

Destination	Time of Departure From London	Expected Time of Arrival at Destination
Leicester	08:05	09:30
Eastbourne	13:25	14:50
Brighton	15:10	16:05
York	17:05	19:30
Northampton	18:35	20:00

i How long does it take to go from London to Leicester? 1 h 25 mins

ii June took the train from London to Brighton. June's mother took a later train and arrived in Brighton at 21:35. Her journey took the same amount of time as June's. What time did the train that her mother took depart from London? 20:40

iii Mr Lim took the train to York. His train was delayed for 45 minutes. What time did Mr Lim finally arrive in York? 20:15

iv Miss Bell was on the train to Eastbourne when she was told that due to bad weather, they would be arriving in Eastbourne later than expected. She finally arrived in Eastbourne at 15:15. How long was the journey? 1 h 50 mins

Practice Book 4B, p.81

96

Objectives of activities

- *Maths Journal* enables pupils to express their understanding of or difficulty with the concepts, skills and processes they have learnt in this topic.
- This *Put On Your Thinking Caps!* question enables pupils to apply the heuristic of drawing a diagram (a time line) to solve the problem.

Heuristic for problem solving

Draw a diagram

Independent work

Challenging Practice and *Problem Solving* in Practice Book 4B, pp 87 to 88.

Maths Journal

28 The list below shows what has been covered in this unit. Write down which parts of this unit you like the most and which parts you find difficult.

24-hour clock:

a Change time from 12-hour clock to 24-hour clock.

b Change time from 24-hour clock to 12-hour clock.

c Find duration.

d Find the end time.

e Find the start time.

Put On Your Thinking Caps!

29 Mr Green got off a train at 00:30 on Saturday. His journey was 55 minutes long. At what time did he get on board the train? What day was it?

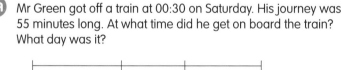

23:00   ?   00:00   00:30

Mr Green got on the train at [23:35]. It was [Friday].

| Practice Book 4B, p.87 | Practice Book 4B, p.88 |

97

Teaching sequence

28 *Maths Journal*

- In this task, pupils express their understanding of or difficulty with the concepts, skills and processes they have learnt in this topic of the 24-hour clock.

29 *Put On Your Thinking Caps!*

- Pupils make use of the strategy of drawing a diagram (the time line) to solve the problem.

Time

Date: _____

Practice 1   Seconds

1 How many seconds does it take the second hand of a clock to move from:

a   12 to 1?   _____ 5 _____ s

b   12 to 5?   _____ 25 _____ s

c   12 to 11?   _____ 55 _____ s

d   3 to 8?   _____ 25 _____ s

e   6 to 10?   _____ 20 _____ s

f   9 to 2?   _____ 25 _____ s

2 How many seconds does it take the second hand of a clock to make:

a   one complete turn round the clock?   _____ 60 _____ s

b   a quarter turn round the clock?   _____ 15 _____ s

c   a three-quarter turn round the clock?   _____ 45 _____ s

d   a one and a half turn round the clock?   _____ 90 _____ s

e   two complete turns round the clock?   _____ 120 _____ s

Practice 2   24-hour clock

1. For each of the following, write down the possible times using the 12-hour and 24-hour clocks.

a)

12-hour clock	24-hour clock
9:30 a.m.	09:30
9:30 p.m.	21:30

b)

12-hour clock	24-hour clock
4:45 a.m.	04:45
4:45 p.m.	16:45

c)

12-hour clock	24-hour clock
12:05 a.m.	00:05
12:05 p.m.	12:05

d)

12-hour clock	24-hour clock
7:22 a.m.	07:22
7:22 p.m.	19:22

3. Look at the clock faces below. Fill in the boxes.

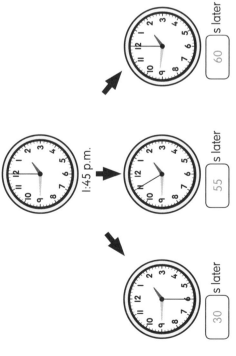

1:45 p.m.

55 s later

30 s later

60 s later

4. Look at the clock faces. Draw the missing minute and second hands on each clock. Then fill in the boxes.

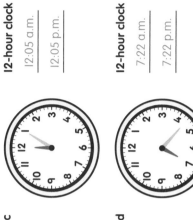

after 40 s

5:10 p.m.

after 50 s

5:11 p.m.

after 30 s

5:12 p.m.

2 Write down the times using either the 12-hour or 24-hour clock. Match the letters to the answers below to answer the question.

12-hour clock		24-hour clock
N	6:30 a.m.	B 06:30
J	8:45 a.m.	E 08:45
	11:15 a.m.	11:15
	12:30 p.m.	12:30
	6:05 p.m.	G 18:05
	7:45 p.m.	I 19:45
B	10:05 p.m.	22:05

What is a popular tourist attraction in London?

B	I	G	B	E	N
10:05 p.m.	19:45	18:05	06:30	08:45	11:15 a.m.

3 On the timeline below, use a cross (X) to show the following times. Then write the time above each cross.

a 08:00   b 12:30   c 16:45

06:00 — 08:00 X
12:00 X 12:30
16:45 X — 18:00

4 On the timeline below, use a cross (X) to show the following times. Then write the time above each cross.

a 14:00   b 18:15   c 21:55

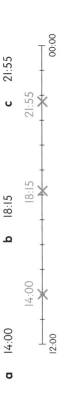

12:00 — 14:00 X
14:00 18:15 X
21:55 X — 00:00

5 Mr Thomas walked from Town A to Town E. The diagram below shows the time he left Town A and the times he reached Towns B to E.

A   B   C   D   E
10:00 10:42 11:56 14:25 ?

a The time Mr Thomas took to walk from:

Town A to Town B is ___0___ h ___42___ mins.

Town B to Town C is ___1___ h ___14___ mins.

Town C to Town D is ___2___ h ___29___ mins.

b Mr Thomas took 7 hours 15 minutes to walk from Town D to Town E.

He reached Town E at ___21:40___ .

Solve these word problems.

6 a Jack began his dance lesson at 17:30. The lesson lasted 45 minutes. What time did the lesson end?

45mins
30mins   15mins
17:30   18:00   18:15

The lesson ended at 18:15.

b A maths test began at 11:35. Ruby finished the test in 55 minutes. What time did Ruby finish her maths test?

55mins
25mins   30mins
11:35   12:00   12:30

Ruby finished her maths test at 12:30.

7

a Miss Brook walks from her house to the bus stop every day.
She leaves home at 06:52 and reaches the bus stop at 07:15.
How long does Miss Brook take to walk from her house to the bus stop?

```
      8mins   15mins
    |——|————————|
  06:52 07:00  07:15
```

Miss Brook takes 23 minutes to walk from her house to the bus stop.

b A film started at 21:45 and ended at 00:36 the next day.
How long was the film?

```
   15mins    1h        1h       36mins
  |——|————————|————————|————————|
 21:45 22:00  23:00   00:00    00:36
```

The film was 2 h 51 mins long.

c It started raining at 22:30 on Friday. The rain ended at 01:15 the next day. How long did it rain for?

```
   30mins     1h         1h      15mins
  |——|————————|————————|——|
 22:30 23:00  00:00    01:00 01:15
```

It rained for 2 h 45 mins.

8

a A disco ended at 23:05. The disco lasted 3 h and 10 mins.
What time did the disco start?

```
       1h        1h        1h     10mins
  |————————|————————|————————|——|
 19:55    20:55    21:55    22:55 23:05
```

The disco started at 19:55.

b Ella attended a lesson at a club. The lesson was 2 h and 25 mins long. Her lesson ended at 10:35. What time did it start?

```
       1h        1h      25mins
  |————————|————————|——|
 08:10    09:10    10:10 10:35
```

The lesson started at 08:10.

Answers Unit 11: Time

Challenging Practice

1 Ruby's birthday party started on 12 October at 17:45. Her sister's birthday party started 18 hours later. Give the date and time of her sister's birthday party.

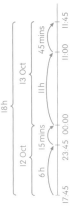

18h

12 Oct	13 Oct
6h	15 mins	11h	45 mins
17:45	23:45	00:00	11:00	11:45

Ruby's sister's birthday party started at 11:45 on 13 October.

2 Peter's birthday party started on Saturday at 20:30. Farha's birthday party started 30 hours earlier. On what day and at what time did Farha's birthday party start?

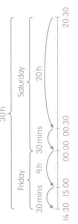

30h

Friday	Saturday
30 mins	9h	30 mins	20h
14:30	15:00	00:00	00:30	20:30

Farha's birthday party started at 14:30 on Friday.

---

c A football match between Rovers United and Aston United lasted 1h and 45 mins. The match ended at 18:45. What time did it start?

1h | 45 mins

17:00 | 18:00 | 18:45

The match started at 17:00.

d Hardeep arrived at the swimming pool at 15:20. He took 42 mins to travel from his house to the pool. What time did he leave his house?

2 mins | 20 mins | 20 mins

14:38 | 14:40 | 15:00 | 15:20

He left his house at 14:38.

Problem Solving

1 When it is 08:00 in Paris, it is 07:00 in London. Millie's friend called her from Paris, where the time was 10:30. What was the time in London?

Paris time   08:00   09:00   10:00   10:30   11:00   11:30

London time   07:00   08:00   09:00   09:30   10:00   10:30

The time in London was 09:30.

2 When it is 08:00 in the UK, it is 10:00 in Greece. A plane took off from the UK at 09:45 and flew to Greece. When it landed in Greece, a clock there showed 15:45. How long did the flight actually take?

UK time   08:00   09:45   10:45   11:45   12:45   13:45   14:45   15:45

Greece time   10:00   12:45   13:45   14:45   15:45

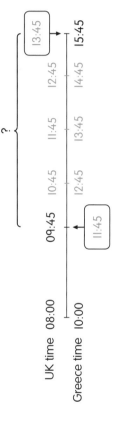

13:45

11:45

?

The flight took 4 hours.

Unit 12: Area and Perimeter

Medium-term plan

Week	Learning Objectives	Thinking Skills	Resources
1	**(1) Rectangles and squares** Pupils will be able to: • recall the formulas to find the perimeter and area of a square and a rectangle • use the formula that the sum of the length and width of a rectangle is half of its perimeter • find the length or width of a rectangle given its perimeter and the width or length respectively • find the side of a square given its perimeter • find the length or width of a rectangle given its area and the width or length respectively • find the side of a square given its area	• Applying concepts of perimeter and area • Relating addition to subtraction and multiplication to division • Identifying relationships • Spatial visualisation	• Pupil Textbook 4B, pp 98 to 103 • Practice Book 4B, pp 89 to 92 • Teacher's Guide 4B, pp 148 to 153

Unit 12: Area and Perimeter

Week	Learning Objectives	Thinking Skills	Resources
1	*Let's Explore!* Pupils will be able to: • investigate whether there is any relationship between the area and the perimeter of a rectangle • determine how the area of a rectangle changes when the length or width is changed		• Pupil Textbook 4B, p 104 • Teacher's Guide 4B, p 154
1–2	**(2) Composite shapes** Pupils will be able to: • find the perimeter of a composite shape made up of squares and/or rectangles • find the area of a composite shape made up of squares and/or rectangles • visualise that a composite shape can be dissected into two or more shapes	• Comparing • Spatial visualisation • Applying concepts of perimeter and area to composite shapes	• Pupil Textbook 4B, pp 105 to 109 • Practice Book 4B, pp 93 to 96 • Teacher's Guide 4B, pp 155 to 159

Unit 12: Area and Perimeter

Medium-term plan

Week	Learning Objectives	Thinking Skills	Resources
2	**(3) Solving word problems** Pupils will be able to: • solve word problems involving composite shapes • apply the strategy 'whole – parts = parts' when solving problems • visualise new and old shapes when a shape has been folded *Let's Explore!* Pupils will be able to visualise that some parts (length or width) do not change when a rectangular piece of paper is folded in a certain way. *Maths Journal* In *Maths Journal*, pupils will be able to recall the skills that they have learnt in this topic.	• Translating verbal statements to diagrammatic representation • Visualising 'part-whole' relationships	• Pupil Textbook 4B, pp 110 to 115 • Practice Book 4B, pp 97 to 98 • Teacher's Guide 4B, pp 160 to 165

Unit 12: Area and Perimeter

Medium-term plan

Week	Learning Objectives	Thinking Skills	Resources
2	*Put On Your Thinking Caps!* In *Put On Your Thinking Caps!* pupils will be able to use the strategies of making a list/table for problems **a** and **d**, and drawing a diagram for problem **b**.	• Spatial visualisation • Comparing Heuristics for problem solving: • Make a systematic list • Draw a diagram • Simplify the problem • Act it out	• Pupil Textbook 4B, pp 115 to 116 • Practice Book 4B, pp 101 to 104 • Teacher's Guide 4B, pp 165 to 166
	Review 6		• Practice Book 4B, pp 105 to 108

Area and Perimeter

Learning objectives: Rectangles and squares

Pupils will be able to:

- recall the formulas to find the perimeter and area of a square and a rectangle
- use the formula that the sum of the length and width of a rectangle is half of its perimeter

Teaching sequence

1

- Review the concept of perimeter by asking pupils to identify the perimeter of some plane closed figures.
- Show pupils a rectangle and ask what the perimeter is equal to in terms of its length and width.
- Guide pupils to see that since Perimeter = (Length + Width) + (Length + Width), Length + Width $= \frac{1}{2} \times$ Perimeter or Perimeter $\div 2$.

2

- Demonstrate how to use the above relationship to find the width of a rectangle given its perimeter and its length.

  Length + Width $= \frac{1}{2} \times 18$ or $18 \div 2 = 9\,cm$

- Use a model to explain the next step:
  6 cm + Width = 9 cm

  Width = 9 − 6 = 3 cm
- Alternatively, use the inverse relationship between addition and subtraction, that is, if $a + b = c$, then $c - a = b$ and $c - b = a$. So if 6 + Width = 9, then 9 − 6 = Width.

- find the length or width of a rectangle given its perimeter and the width or length respectively
- find the side of a square given its perimeter
- find the length or width of a rectangle given its area and the width or length respectively
- find the side of a square given its area

Key concepts

- The perimeter of a plane closed figure is the distance around the figure. For a rectangle, the perimeter is 2 × (Length + Width) and for a square, it is 4 × length of side.
- The area of a plane closed figure is the amount of surface inside the figure. For a rectangle, the area is Length × Width and for a square, it is Side × Side.

Unit 12 **Area and Perimeter**

Let's Learn!

Rectangles and squares

Perimeter

1

Width | Length

Perimeter of rectangle = Length + Width + Length + Width
= Length of all its 4 sides

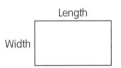

> Using a model, we can show that the perimeter of the rectangle is the sum of its two lengths and two widths.

Perimeter

| Length | Width | Length | Width |

Length + Width | Length + Width

Length + Width of a rectangle is equal to $\frac{1}{2}$ of its perimeter.

2 The perimeter of Rectangle A is 18 cm. Its length is 6 cm. Find its width.

Perimeter = 18 cm
Length + Width = Perimeter $\div$ 2
= 18 $\div$ 2
= 9 cm

6 cm + Width = 9 cm
Width = 9 − 6 = 3 cm

The width of Rectangle A is 3 cm.

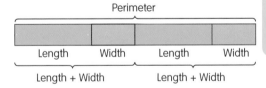

6 cm

? cm

Rectangle A

> Length = 6 cm

---

3 The perimeter of Rectangle B is 28 cm.
Its length is 8 cm. Find its width.

Length + Width = Perimeter ÷ 2

= [28] ÷ [2]

= [14] cm

8 cm + Width = [14] cm

Width = [14] − [8]

= [6] cm

The width of Rectangle B is [6] cm.

8 cm

? cm

Rectangle B

Length = 8 cm

4 The perimeter of a square is 64 cm.
Find the length of a side of the square.

All the sides of a square are equal.
There are 4 sides in a square.
Length of a side = Perimeter ÷ 4

= 64 ÷ 4

= 16 cm

The length of a side of the square is 16 cm.

? cm

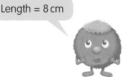

5 Abby bent a piece of wire 132 cm long into a square.
What is the length of a side of the square?

Length of a side = [132] ÷ 4 = [33] cm

The length of a side of the square is [33] cm.

Thinking skills

- Applying concepts of perimeter and area
- Relating addition to subtraction and multiplication to division
- Identifying relationships
- Spatial visualisation

What you will need

Piece of wire

Teaching sequence

3

- Use this question to informally assess pupils' understanding.
- Pupils are expected to apply the method shown in **2** to solve a similar problem.

4

- Guide pupils to recall that all sides of a square are equal.
- Demonstrate how to find the side of a square given its perimeter.
- If necessary, use this model to explain how the side is found.

64 cm

4 × Side = Perimeter

Side = Perimeter ÷ 4

5

- Use this question to informally assess pupils' understanding.
- Pupils are expected to apply the method shown in **4** to solve a similar problem.
- If necessary, bend a piece of wire to make a square to demonstrate that the length of the wire is the perimeter of the square.

Independent work

Practice I in Practice Book 4B,
pp 89 to 90.

Teaching sequence

- Ask pupils to work on these
  questions for further practice.

6 The perimeter of a rectangle is 32 cm. Its width is 5 cm. Find the length
   of the rectangle. II cm

7 The perimeter of a rectangle is I28 cm. Its length is 35 cm. Find the
   width of the rectangle. 29 cm

8 The perimeter of a square is 36 cm. Find the length of one side of
   the square. 9 cm

9 Jack stuck a ribbon of length 72 cm around a box with a square top.
   What is the length of one side of the square top? I8 cm

10 Millie walks 480 m around a rectangular field once. The length of
    the field is I60 m. What is the width of the field? 80 m

Practice Book 4B, p.89

I00

Area

How do you find the area of a rectangle?

Length

Width

Area of rectangle = Length × Width

or

Length × Width = Area of rectangle

12 The area of a rectangular carpet is 63 m². Its length is 9 m. Find its width.

9 m

? cm   Area = 63 m²

Area = 63 m², Length = 9 m

Length × Width = Area

9 m × Width = 63 m²

Width = 63 ÷ 9

= 7 m

Its width is 7 m.

Remember:
9 × 7 = 63

13 The area of a rectangular piece of land is 96 m². Its width is 8 m. Find its length.

Area = [96] m², Width = [8] m

Length × [8] = [96] m²

Length = [96] ÷ [8]

= [12] m

Its length is [12] m.

101

Teaching sequence

11

- Remind pupils of the concept of area by asking them to identify the areas of some plane closed figures.
- Then show pupils a rectangle and ask them to recall what its area is equal to in terms of its length and width.
- Area of a rectangle = Length × Width
- Use the inverse relationship between multiplication and division, i.e. if $a × b = c$, then $c ÷ a = b$ and $c ÷ b = a$, to explain how to find the length or width.
- Write: Length × Width = Area. So Area ÷ Length = Width and Area ÷ Width = Length, i.e. Width = Area ÷ Length and Length = Area ÷ Width.

12

- Demonstrate how to use this relationship to find the width of a rectangle given its area and length. Since 9 × Width = 63, 63 ÷ 9 = Width, i.e. Width = 63 ÷ 9 = 7 m

13

- Use this question to informally assess pupils' understanding. Pupils are expected to apply the method shown in **12** to solve a similar problem.

Teaching sequence

- Guide pupils to recall that:
  Area of a square = Side × Side.
  Ask pupils for the areas of
  squares with sides of 3 cm, 4 cm,
  6 cm, 7 cm, etc. List the areas in
  this way:
  $3 \times 3 = 9 \, cm^2$
  $4 \times 4 = 16 \, cm^2$
  $6 \times 6 = 36 \, cm^2$
  $7 \times 7 = 49 \, cm^2$

  Pupils should notice that the
  area of a square is always the
  product of two equal numbers.

- Discuss with pupils how to find
  the side of a square given its
  area, e.g. 81 cm². Guide pupils
  to understand that the question
  they need to answer is this:
  *What number multiplied by
  itself is equal to 81?*

  Since 9 × 9 = 81, the required
  number is 9 and so the side of
  the square is 9 cm.

15

- Ask pupils to work on these
  questions as a controlled
  practice of using the process in
  14.

---

14 The area of Square A is 25 cm².

   a Find the length of a side of the square.

   b Find the perimeter of the square.

   a   Area = 25 cm²   Area of square
              25 = 5 × 5   = Length × Length
      Length of side = 5 cm   of side of side

Area = 25 cm²

Square A

The length of a side of Square A is 5 cm.

   b Perimeter = 4 × 5   Perimeter of square
             = 20 cm   = 4 × Length of side

The perimeter of Square A is 20 cm.

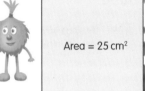

15 The area of Square B is 49 cm².

   a Find the length of a side of the square.

   b Find the perimeter of the square.

   a   Area = 49 cm²   Which number,
                      when multiplied by
        49 = [7] × [7] itself, makes 49?
      Length = [7] cm

The length of a side of

Square B is [7] cm.

Area = 49 cm²

Square B

   b Perimeter = 4 × [7]

            = [28] cm

The perimeter of Square B is [28] cm.

102

Independent work

Practice 2 in Practice Book 4B,
pp 91 to 92.

---

16 The area of a rectangular garden is 48 m². Its length is 8 m.
Find its width. 6 m

17 The area of a square tile is 81 cm². Find the length of a side
of the square tile. 9 cm

| ?cm | 81 cm² |

18 The area of a rectangular picture is 108 cm². Its width is 9 cm.

   a Find its length. 12 cm

   b Find the perimeter of the picture. 42 cm

19 The area of a square kitchen is 16 m².

   a Find the length of a side of the kitchen. 4 m

   b Find the perimeter of the kitchen. 16 m

20 The perimeter of a square garden is 24 m.

   a Find the length of its side. 6 m

   b Find the area of the garden. 36 m²

21 The perimeter of a rectangle is 36 m. Its length is twice as long
as its width.

   a Find the length and width of the rectangle. Length = 12 m,

   b Find the area of the rectangle. 72 m² Width = 6 m

 Home Maths — Encourage your child to try to find the perimeter and area of an
object at home. You could use the cover of a book or the front of
a cereal box. By measuring the length and width of the object
to the nearest centimetre, they should be able to calculate the
perimeter and the area.

Practice Book 4B, p.91

103

Teaching sequence

16 and **17**

- Ask pupils to work on these
  questions for further practice.

18

- This is a two-step word problem.
  The first step requires pupils to
  apply the method taught in **12**.
  The second step requires pupils
  to apply the formula for finding
  the perimeter of a rectangle.

19

- This is a two-step word
  problem. The first step requires
  pupils to apply the method
  taught in **14**. The second
  step requires pupils to apply
  the formula for finding the
  perimeter of a square.

20

- This is a two-step word problem.
  The first step requires pupils to
  find the side of a square given
  its perimeter. The second step
  requires pupils to apply the
  formula for finding the area of
  a square.

21

- This problem can be solved by
  drawing a model to show that
  the perimeter of the rectangle
  is made up of 6 equal units.

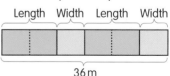

| Length | Width | Length | Width |

36 m

6 units = 36 m
1 unit = 36 ÷ 6 = 6 m
Width of rectangle = 6 m
Length of rectangle = 6 × 2
= 12 m
Area of rectangle = 6 × 12
= 72 m²

Unit 12: Area and Perimeter   153

Objective of activity

Pupils will be able to:

- investigate whether there is any relationship between the area and the perimeter of a rectangle
- determine how the area of a rectangle changes when the length or width is changed

What you will need

- Geoboards
- Rubber bands
- Square dotty paper

Teaching sequence

22 *Let's Explore!*

- Ask pupils to work in groups.
- This is an investigative activity for pupils to explore whether there is any relationship between area and perimeter.
- Pupils should make as many different rectangles with the same perimeter as possible and calculate their areas. Ask pupils "What is special about Rectangle A?"
- Guide pupils to see that the rectangles made have the same perimeter but different areas.

Let's Explore!

22 Work in groups of four.
You will need a geoboard and some rubber bands.
Make as many different rectangles as possible on the geoboard.
Make sure that all the rectangles you make have the same perimeter.
Then write down your answers like this:

> You may also use square dotty paper.

Example

Rectangle	Length	Width	Perimeter	Area
A	3 cm	3 cm	12 cm	9 cm²
B	4 cm	2 cm	12 cm	8 cm²

What do you notice about the area of these rectangles?
They have different areas.

Learning objectives: Composite shapes

Pupils will be able to:

- find the perimeter of a composite shape made up of squares and/or rectangles
- find the area of a composite shape made up of squares and/or rectangles
- visualise that a composite shape can be dissected into two or more shapes

Key concepts

- The perimeter of a composite shape is the total distance around it.
- The area of a composite shape is the sum of the areas of all the individual rectangles and squares that make up the composite shape.
- Area of a rectangle = Length × Width and Area of a square = Side × Side.
- Opposite sides of a rectangle are equal.
- The four sides of a square are equal.

Thinking skills

- Comparing
- Spatial visualisation
- Applying concepts of perimeter and area to composite shapes

Teaching sequence

- Show pupils some examples of composite shapes made up of rectangles and/or squares.
- Explain to pupils that the perimeter of a composite shape is the total distance around it.
- In example ❶, guide pupils to identify the perimeter of the piece of land ABCDEF. Then show pupils how to partition the composite shape into a square and a rectangle or two rectangles.

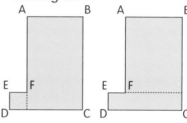

- In either diagram, encourage pupils to see that they have to first find the lengths CD and AF before they can find the perimeter of the land.
- Encourage pupils to recall these properties of squares and rectangles: opposite sides of a rectangle are equal and the four sides of a square are equal.
- Using either diagram, ask pupils what CD and AF are equal to. Guide pupils to see that CD = EF + AB and AF = BC − DE. Then demonstrate how the perimeter can be found by adding the sides of the figure.

Let's Learn!

Composite shapes

❶

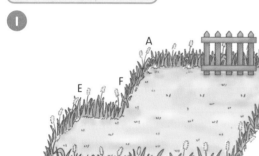

A farmer wants to put a fence up around the piece of land ABCDEF. What is the perimeter of the land?

What are the lengths of CD and AF?

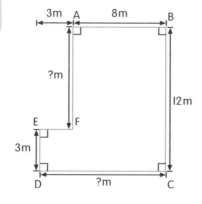

CD = EF + AB
   = 3 + 8
   = 11 m

AF = BC − DE
   = 12 − 3
   = 9 m

Perimeter of land ABCDEF = AB + BC + CD + DE + EF + AF
                         = 8 + 12 + 11 + 3 + 3 + 9
                         = 46 m

105

Teaching sequence

- Ask pupils to work on this question as a controlled practice.

3

- Ask pupils to work on these questions to informally assess their understanding.

---

2 Find the perimeter of the shape ABCDEF.

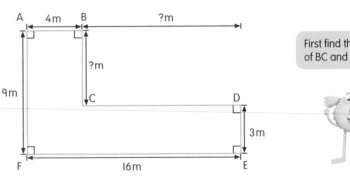

First find the length of BC and CD.

BC = AF − DE

= [9] − [3]

= [6] m

CD = [EF] − [AB]

= [16] − [4]

= [12] m

BC + DE = AF
AB + CD = EF

Perimeter of shape ABCDEF

= [AB] + [BC] + [CD] + [DE] + [EF] + [AF]

= [4] + [6] + [12] + [3] + [16] + [9]

= [50] m

3 Find the perimeter of each shape. (All lines meet at right angles.)

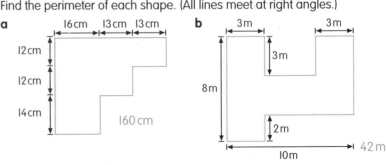

106

4 Find the area of the shape below.

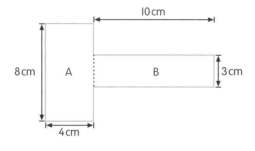

This shape is made up of 2 or more smaller rectangles. It is called a **composite shape**.

Area of Rectangle = Length × Width
Area of Rectangle A = $8 \times 4 = 32 \, cm^2$
Area of Rectangle B = $10 \times 3 = 30 \, cm^2$
Area of the shape = Area of Rectangle A + Area of Rectangle B
= 32 + 30
= $62 \, cm^2$

5 Find the area of the shape below.
It is made up of a square and a rectangle.

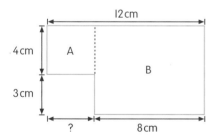

I can also divide the shape into two rectangles like this.

How do I find the area now?

Area of Square A = $\boxed{4}$ × $\boxed{4}$
= $\boxed{16}$ cm^2

Area of Rectangle B = $\boxed{8}$ × $\boxed{7}$
= $\boxed{56}$ cm^2

Area of the shape = $\boxed{16}$ + $\boxed{56}$ = $\boxed{72}$ cm^2

I07

Teaching sequence

4

- Demonstrate to pupils how to find the area of a composite shape.
- Show pupils that the composite shape can be partitioned into two rectangles, A and B. Ask pupils what the area of the composite shape is equal to.
- Guide pupils through the steps in the solution.

5

- Ask pupils to work on this question as a controlled practice. Remind them that in this question, the unknown side of the rectangle has to be found first.

Additional activity

Ask pupils to work in pairs. Give each pair a square with sides of 4 cm and a square with sides of 6 cm. Ask each pair to make three different types of composite shapes. Then ask them to calculate the areas and perimeters of each composite shape.

The shapes that can be made with the two squares:

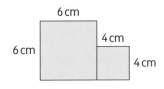

Area = 52 cm²
Perimeter = 32 cm

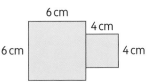

Area = 52 cm²
Perimeter = 32 cm

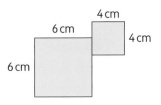

Area = 52 cm²
Perimeter = unknown

Teaching sequence

- Ask pupils to work on these questions to informally assess their understanding.

6 Trace the shapes below. Add dotted lines to divide each shape into rectangles or squares. Then find the area of each shape.

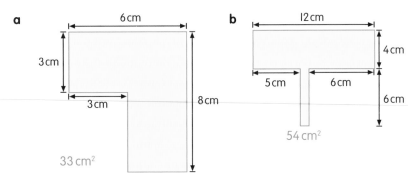

a

33 cm²

b

54 cm²

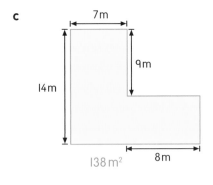

c

138 m²

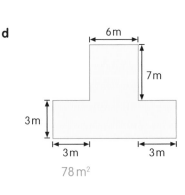

d

78 m²

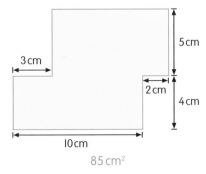

e

85 cm²

What you will need

- Sheets of paper
- Rulers
- Scissors

Independent work

Practice 3 in Practice Book 4B, pp 93 to 96.

Activity

7 Work in pairs.

You will need some sheets of paper, a ruler and a pair of scissors.

1 Draw two rectangles on a sheet of paper and cut them out.

2 Draw one rectangle and one square on a sheet of paper and cut them out.

3 Draw two rectangles and one square on a sheet of paper and cut them out.

4 Make as many different shapes as you can using each set of cut-outs.

Example

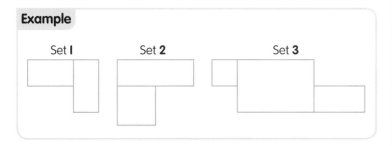

Set **1**   Set **2**   Set **3**

5 Then draw the shapes you made on another sheet of paper. Compare your shapes with those of your friends.

6 Alternatively, you could use a computer to draw the squares and rectangles and put them together.

Practice Book 4B, p.93

109

Teaching sequence

- This activity reinforces pupils' understanding of composite shapes by asking them to create different composite shapes with squares and rectangles.

- Guide pupils through the process of solving word problems:
- **Step 1**
  Read the problem carefully and identify the given and implied (if any) information and what is to be found. If necessary, draw a diagram to help pupils understand the problem (in this section, all diagrams are provided).
- The figure in the textbook shows a small rectangle BCDG inside a big rectangle ACEF. *Since AB = 5 cm and BC = 4 cm, what does this imply? AC = 9 cm. Similarly, CD = 3 cm and DE = 2 cm. What does this imply? What is to be found?*
- **Step 2**
  Think of a strategy to use, e.g. write a number sentence, simplify the problem, draw a diagram/model, make a list, etc. In this problem, the strategy to be used comes from the diagram, where it can be seen that the required area is the difference between the areas of the two rectangles.
- **Step 3**
  Solve the problem by carrying out the strategy. In this case, finding the areas of rectangles ACEF and BCDG and using subtraction will give the solution.
- **Step 4**
  If necessary, check the answer. This can usually be done by working back. In this case, adding the areas of the shaded part and rectangle BCDG should give the area of rectangle ACEF.

2

- Ask pupils to work on this question as a controlled practice.

Learning objectives:
Solving word problems

Pupils will be able to:

- solve word problems involving composite shapes
- apply the strategy 'whole – parts = parts' when solving problems
- visualise new and old shapes when a shape has been folded

Key concept

Application of the concepts of area and perimeter of squares and rectangles to solving word problems

Thinking skills

- Translating verbal statements to diagrammatic representation
- Visualising 'part-whole' relationships

Unit 12 Area and Perimeter

Let's Learn!

Solving word problems

1 The shape shows a small rectangle BCDG and a big rectangle ACEF. Find the area of the shaded part of the shape.

| Area of shaded part | = | Area of big rectangle | – | Area of small rectangle |

Length of big rectangle = AC = 5 + 4 = 9 cm
Width of big rectangle   = CE = 3 + 2 = 5 cm
Area of big rectangle   = 9 × 5 = 45 cm²
Area of small rectangle = 4 × 3 = 12 cm²
Area of shaded part   = 45 – 12 = 33 cm²

2 The shape shows a small rectangle BCGH and a big rectangle ADEF. Find the area of the shaded part of the shape.

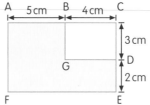
First find the area of the big rectangle.

Length of big rectangle = [2] + [4] + [2]

= [8] cm

Width of big rectangle = [6] cm

Area of big rectangle = [8] × [6] = [48] cm²

Area of small rectangle = [4] × [3] = [12] cm²

Area of shaded part = [48] – [12] = [36] cm²

110

3 The shape shows a rectangular field with a path 2 m wide around it.
Find the area of the path.

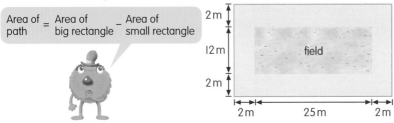

Area of path = Area of big rectangle − Area of small rectangle

2 m
12 m   field
2 m

2 m   25 m   2 m

Length of big rectangle   = 25 + 2 + 2 = 29 m
Width of big rectangle   = 12 + 2 + 2 = 16 m
Area of big rectangle   = 29 × 16 = 464 m²
Area of small rectangle   = 25 × 12 = 300 m²
Area of path   = 464 − 300 = 164 m²

4 A rectangular piece of cloth measures 80 cm by 60 cm.
When it is placed on a table, it leaves a margin 5 cm wide all around it.
Find the area of the table not covered by the cloth.

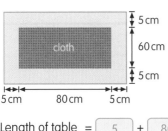

5 cm
cloth   60 cm
5 cm

5 cm   80 cm   5 cm

Area of table not covered by cloth
= Area of table − Area of cloth

Length of table = [5] + [80] + [5] = [90] cm

Width of table = [5] + [60] + [5] = [70] cm

Area of table   = [90] × [70] = [6300] cm²

Area of cloth   = [80] × [60] = [4800] cm²

Area of table not covered by cloth = [6300] − [4800]

= [1500] cm²

Teaching sequence

3

- Ask pupils to compare the shapes in **1** and **3**. Encourage them to talk about the differences and similarities.
- You could use one big rectangle and one small rectangle to demonstrate how the shapes in **1** and **3** can be made by placing the small rectangle in one corner or in the middle of the big rectangle.
- Explain that the same strategy can be used to solve the two problems, both of which involve the 'part-whole' concept.

4

- Ask pupils to work on this question to informally assess their understanding.

III

Teaching sequence

- Encourage pupils to discuss the problem. They should be able to use the 'part-whole' concept to solve the problem.
- The big rectangle is a whole. The cut-out rectangle is a part of it. The remaining part is also part of the big rectangle. Remaining part = whole – part (cut-out rectangle)

- Assess pupils' ability to apply the 'part-whole' concept to solve a similar problem.

5 Hardeep has a sheet of paper 13 cm long and 8 cm wide.
He cuts away a small rectangle at one of its corners.
The length and width of the small rectangle are shown in the shape.

a Find the area of the remaining paper. 74 cm²

b Find the perimeter of the remaining paper. 42 cm

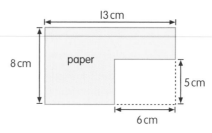

6 Sophie laid a path 1·5 m wide around a rectangular piece of land.
The length and width of the outer path are shown in the shape.

a Find the area of the rectangular land. 273 m²

b Find the perimeter of the rectangular land. 68 m

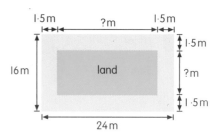

What you will need
- 7 cm by 7 cm square piece of paper
- 10 cm by 5 cm rectangular piece of paper

Teaching sequence

7

- Demonstrate to pupils that the length, 2 cm, of the triangle is part of one side of the square made by folding and unfolding a piece of square paper.

8

- Ask pupils to solve the problem by folding a rectangular piece of paper, 10 cm by 5 cm, as shown in the textbook.

7 A corner of a square piece of paper is folded.

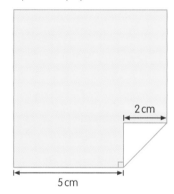

2 cm

5 cm

a What is the perimeter of the unfolded square piece of paper?

b What is the area of the unfolded square piece of paper?

a A side of the square = 5 + 2
$$= 7 \text{ cm}$$
Perimeter of the square = 4 × 7
$$= 28 \text{ cm}$$

b Area of the square = 7 × 7
$$= 49 \text{ cm}^2$$

8 A rectangular piece of paper is folded at one of its corners so that the edge BC lies along the edge CD as shown.

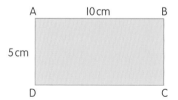
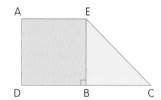

a What is the area of the rectangle before it is folded? 50 cm²

b What fraction of the area of the rectangle is the area of the shape AECBD? $\frac{3}{4}$

113

Unit 12: Area and Perimeter 163

Objective of activity

Pupils will be able to visualise that some parts (length or width) do not change when a rectangular piece of paper is folded in a certain way.

What you will need

8 cm by 6 cm rectangular piece of paper

Independent work

Practice 4 in Practice Book 4B, pp 97 to 100.

Teaching sequence

9 *Let's Explore!*

- Pupils explore how the area of a rectangle changes when either the length or width is changed.
- The objective of the activity is to help pupils realise that one of the sides is not changed and they only need to measure the other side to find the area of the new rectangle made.

Let's Explore!

9

1   Cut out a rectangle 8 cm long and 6 cm wide.

2   Draw this rectangle on a sheet of paper and label its length and width. Find its area.

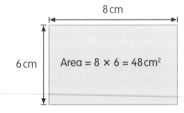

8 cm

6 cm

Area = 8 × 6 = 48 cm²

3   Fold the cut-out rectangle to make a rectangular shape. Measure the length and width of this shape. Find its area. Two examples of folded rectangles are shown below.

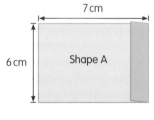

7 cm

6 cm

Shape A

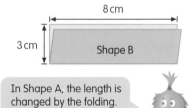

8 cm

3 cm

Shape B

In Shape A, the length is changed by the folding. In Shape B, the width is changed by the folding.

4   Unfold the rectangle you made in **3**. Fold it to make another rectangular shape. This time take only one measurement – measure the side that is changed by the folding. Then find the area of the folded rectangle.

5   Check your answer by measuring the length and width of the folded rectangle.

6   Make two more rectangular shapes with the cut-out rectangle. Take only one measurement for each shape as in **4**. Then find its area.

7   Does your method of using one measurement to find the area apply for these shapes too?

Practice Book 4B, p.97

114

Objective of activity

- In *Maths Journal*, pupils will be able to recall the skills that they have learnt in this topic.
- In *Put On Your Thinking Caps!* pupils will be able to use the strategies of making a list/ table for problems **a** and **d**, and drawing a diagram for problem **b**.

Thinking skills

- Spatial visualisation
- Comparing

Heuristics for problem solving

- Make a systematic list
- Draw a diagram
- Simplify the problem
- Act it out

Teaching sequence

10 *Maths Journal*

- Pupils express their understanding of or difficulty with the processes they have been taught.

11 *Put On Your Thinking Caps!*

a

- Ask pupils to make a list/table of the lengths, perimeters and areas of squares.

Length of side (cm)	1	2	3	4	5	6
Perimeter of square (cm)	4	8	12	16	20	24
Area of square (cm²)	1	4	9	16	25	36

- When the length of the side is 4 cm, the perimeter and the area have the same numerical value, 16.

b

- Ask pupils to draw the rectangle. Then mark 3 cm intervals:
  (i) along the length of 12 cm

  (ii) along the width of 8 cm

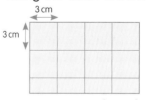

- The maximum number of squares of sides 3 cm that can be drawn is 8.

c

- Guide pupils to see that the perimeter of the shape is that of a rectangle 25 cm by 12 cm.

Area and Perimeter **Unit 12**

Maths Journal

10 The list below shows what has been covered in this unit. Write down which parts of this unit you like the most and which parts you find difficult.

Area and Perimeter

a Find the length of one side of a rectangle given its perimeter and the other side.

b Find the length of the sides of a square given its perimeter.

c Find the length of one side of a rectangle given its area and the other side.

d Find the length of the sides of a square given its area.

e Find the perimeter of a composite shape.

f Find the area of a composite shape by dividing the shape into different types of rectangles.

Put On Your Thinking Caps!

11 **a** What is the length of the side of a square if its perimeter and area have the same numerical value? 4 cm
(Hint: Make a systematic list.)

b Ella has a rectangular piece of paper 12 cm long and 8 cm wide. How many squares can she draw on the piece of paper, without overlapping, if the side of each square is 3 cm long? 8

c Look at the shape. All sides of the shape meet at right angles. What is the perimeter of the shape?
74 cm

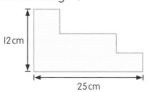

115

Independent work

Challenging Practice, Problem Solving and Review 6 in Practice Book 4B, pp 101 to 108.

Teaching sequence

d

- Ask pupils to make a list of the sides of the squares and their areas. Ask pupils why the list of the sides doesn't need to extend beyond 10 cm.
- From the list of areas, pupils have to find a pair that will add up to 89 cm². Ask pupils how they can do this using logical reasoning.
- The ones digits of the areas are 1, 4, 5, 6, and 9 (0 does not need to be considered as 100 is clearly more than 89). To get 89, the sum of the ones digits must end in 9. Thus, the only possible pairs are 4 + 25 and 25 + 64.
- The areas of the two squares are 25 cm² and 64 cm² and the sides are 5 cm and 8 cm respectively.

Put On Your Thinking Caps!

d Jack arranged two different square pieces of paper as shown. The length of the side of each square piece of paper is a whole number.

The total area of the shape is 89 cm². What is the length of the side of each square piece of paper? Copy the table below and complete it to find out the answer.

Length of the Square (cm)	1	2	3	4	5	6	7	8	9	10
Area of the Square (cm²)	1	4	9							

a The side of the square is 4 cm.

1st Guess
Area = 2 × 2 = 4 cm²
Perimeter = 4 × 2 = 8 cm
4 is not equal to 8 numerically.
So the side is not 2 cm.

2nd Guess
Area = 4 × 4 = 16 cm²
Perimeter = 4 × 4 = 16 cm
16 is equal to 16.
So the side of the square is 4 cm.

b She can draw eight 3 cm squares on the rectangular paper.
On the 12 cm long side, mark 3 cm intervals.
There are 4 equal intervals of length 3 cm each in total.
On the 8 cm long side, mark 3 cm intervals.
There are 2 equal intervals of length 3 cm each, with 2 cm left over as the last interval.

Total number of 3 cm squares
= 4 × 2 = 8

c The perimeter of the shape is 74 cm.
Length of horizontal side = 25 cm
Sum of lengths of horizontal lines
= 2 × 25 = 50 cm
Length of vertical side = 12 cm
Sum of lengths of vertical lines
= 2 × 12 = 24 cm
Perimeter of shape = 50 + 24 = 74 cm

d The sides of the square papers are 5 cm and 8 cm respectively.
The total area of the shape comprises 2 squares.
Each square has one of the areas in the completed table.
Which 2 squares make 89 cm²?
25 + 64 = 89 cm²
Therefore the sides of the 2 squares are 5 cm and 8 cm respectively.

Practice Book 4B, p.101   Practice Book 4B, p.103

116

Area and Perimeter

Unit 12

Date: _____

Practice 1   Rectangles and squares

1 Find the perimeter of the following shapes.

a

7 cm
4 cm

Perimeter of rectangle

$= \underline{\quad 7 \quad} + \underline{\quad 7 \quad} + \underline{\quad 4 \quad} + \underline{\quad 4 \quad}$

$= \underline{\quad 22 \quad}$ cm

b

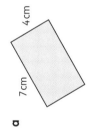

6 cm

Perimeter of square $= 4 \times \underline{\quad 6 \quad}$

$= \underline{\quad 24 \quad}$ cm

2 The perimeter of a square is 20 cm.
Find the length of one side of the square.

Length of one side of the square $= 20 \div 4$

$= 5\,\text{cm}$

? cm

Perimeter = 20 cm

3 The perimeter of a square is 38 cm.
Find the length of one side of the square.

Length of one side of the square $= 38 \div 4$

$= 9.5\,\text{cm}$

? cm

Perimeter = 38 cm

Unit 12: Area and Perimeter

89

Answers Unit 12: Area and Perimeter

167

Date: _____

Practice 2 Rectangles and squares

1 Find the area of the following shapes.

a [12 cm × 6 cm rectangle]

Area of the rectangle = 12 × 6
= 72 cm²

b [9 cm square]

Area of the square = 9 × 9
= 81 cm²

2 The area of a rectangle is 78 cm². Its width is 6 cm. Find its length.

Area = 78 cm²

Length = 13 cm

3 A rectangle has an area of 60 cm². Its length is 8 cm. Find its width.

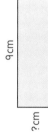

Area = 60 cm²

Width = 7·5 cm

4 The area of a rectangular carpet is 80·5 m². Its width is 7 m.

a Find the length of the carpet.

b Find the perimeter of the carpet.

Area = 80·5 m²

a Length = 80·5 ÷ 7
= 11·5 m

b Perimeter = 11·5 + 11·5 + 7 + 7
= 37 m

---

4 A square field has a perimeter of 42·8 m. Find the length of one side of the field.

Length of one side of the field = 42·8 ÷ 4
= 10·7 m

[square, ?m] Perimeter = 42·8 m

5 The perimeter of a rectangle is 32 cm. Its width is 5 cm. Find its length.

2 × length of the rectangle = 32 – 5 – 5
= 22 cm

Length of the rectangle = 22 ÷ 2
= 11 cm

[rectangle, ?cm, 5 cm] Perimeter = 32 cm

6 The perimeter of a rectangle is 24 cm. Its length is 9 cm. Find its width.

2 × width of the rectangle = 24 – 9 – 9
= 6 cm

Width of the rectangle = 6 ÷ 2
= 3 cm

[rectangle, 9 cm, ?cm]

7 The perimeter of a rectangular garden is 18 m. Its length is 6 m. Find its width.

2 × width of garden = 18 – 6 – 6
= 6 m

Width of garden = 6 ÷ 2
= 3 m

[rectangle, 6 m, ?m] Perimeter = 18 m

Date: _____

Practice 3 Composite shapes

1 Find the missing lengths of the sides of each shape. Then find the perimeter of each shape. (All lines meet at right angles.)

a

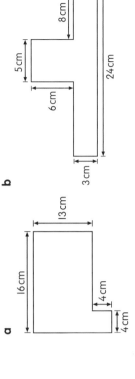

Perimeter = ___66___ cm

b

Perimeter = ___66___ cm

2 Find the perimeter of the shape ABCDEF.

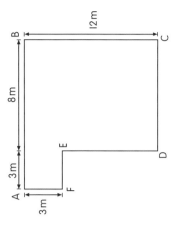

Perimeter = ___46___ m

---

5 The area of a square is 64 cm². Find the length of one side of the square.
(Hint: What number multiplied by itself is equal to 64?)

$8 \times 8 = 64$

Length of one side of the square = 8 cm

6 The area of a square garden is 100 m².
a Find the length of each side of the garden.
b Find the perimeter of the garden.

a $10 \times 10 = 100$
Length of each side = 10 m

b Perimeter = 4×10
= 40 m

7 The area of a rectangle is 45 cm². Its width is 5 cm.
a Find its length.
b Find its perimeter.

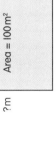

a Length = $45 \div 5$
= 9 cm

b Perimeter = $9 + 9 + 5 + 5$
= 28 cm

8 The perimeter of a rectangle is 156 cm. Its width is 36 cm.
a What is its length?
b Find its area.

a $2 \times$ Length = $156 - 36 - 36$
= 84 cm

Length = $84 \div 2$
= 42 cm

b Area = 42×36
= 1512 cm²

5 Find the perimeter of the shape. (All lines meet at right angles.)

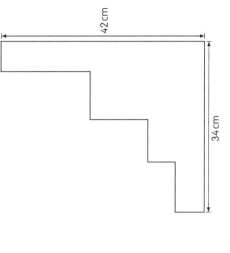

42 cm

34 cm

Perimeter = _____152_____ cm

6 Divide this shape into two rectangles as shown. Then find the area of the whole shape.

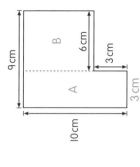

9 cm

10 cm

A

B

6 cm

3 cm

3 cm

Area = _____72_____ cm²

3 A farmer wants to put a fence around the piece of land ABCDEF. Find the perimeter of the piece of land to find the length of fencing he needs.

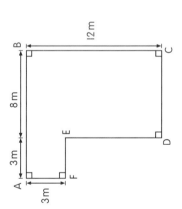

A

3 m

8 m

B

12 m

C

3 m

F

E

D

Perimeter = _____46_____ m

4 Find the perimeter of the following shape. (All lines meet at right angles.)

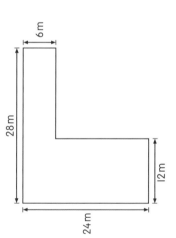

6 m

28 m

24 m

12 m

Perimeter = _____104_____ m

Practice 4 Solving word problems

1 This shape shows a small rectangle and a big rectangle. Find the area of the shaded part of the shape.

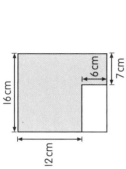

16 cm
12 cm
6 cm
7 cm

Area of big rectangle = __16__ × __18__ = __288__ cm²

Area of small rectangle = __6__ × __9__ = __54__ cm²

Area of shaded part = Area of big rectangle – Area of small rectangle

= __288__ – __54__ = __234__ cm²

2 This shape shows a small rectangle and a big rectangle. Find the area of the shaded part of the shape.

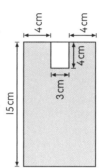

15 cm
4 cm
4 cm
3 cm
4 cm

Area of big rectangle = __15__ × __11__ = __165__ cm²

Area of small rectangle = __3__ × __4__ = __12__ cm²

Area of shaded part = __165__ – __12__ = __153__ cm²

---

7 Find the area of each composite shape. (All lines meet at right angles.)

a

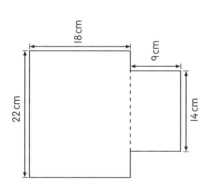

22 cm
18 cm
9 cm
14 cm

Area = __522__ cm²

b

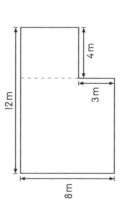

12 m
4 m
3 m
8 m

Area = __84__ m²

3 A carpet is laid on a rectangular floor with a length of 9 m and a width of 6 m. This leaves a 1 m wide margin around the carpet. Find the area of the carpet.

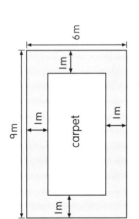

Length of carpet = 9 − 1 − 1
$\qquad$ = 7 m

Width of carpet = 6 − 1 − 1
$\qquad$ = 4 m

Area of carpet = 7 × 4
$\qquad$ = 28 m²

4 A rectangular pond with a length of 18 m and a width of 8 m is surrounded by a path 2 m wide as shown. Find the area of the path.

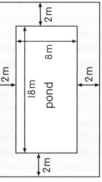

Area of big rectangle = 22 × 12
$\qquad$ = 264 m²

Area of pond = 18 × 8
$\qquad$ = 144 m²

Area of path = 264 − 144
$\qquad$ = 120 m²

---

5 A picture frame measuring 25 cm by 15 cm is made from wood 3 cm wide. Find the area and perimeter of the picture.

Length of picture = 25 − 3 − 3
$\qquad$ = 19 cm

Width of picture = 15 − 3 − 3
$\qquad$ = 9 cm

Area of picture = 19 × 9
$\qquad$ = 171 cm²

Perimeter of picture = 19 + 19 + 9 + 9
$\qquad$ = 56 cm

6 Farha has a piece of cardboard measuring 90 cm by 80 cm. She cuts out a small rectangular piece measuring 15 cm by 20 cm.

a Find the area of the remaining piece of cardboard.

b Find the perimeter of the remaining piece of cardboard.

a 80 × 90 = 7200 cm²
15 × 20 = 300 cm²
7200 − 300 = 6900 cm²

The area of the remaining piece of cardboard is 6900 cm².

b 90 + 80 + 75 + 60 + 15 + 20 = 340 cm

The perimeter of the remaining piece of cardboard is 340 cm.

Challenging Practice

1 The length of a rectangle is 3 times its width. Its perimeter is 64 cm. Find its length.

3 units

8 units → 64 cm
1 unit → 64 ÷ 8 = 8
Width = 8 cm

Length of the rectangle = 3 × 8
= 24 cm

2 The length of a rectangle is twice its width. Its area is 50 cm^2. Find its length and its width.

Using Guess and Check:

Length	Width	Area
8 cm	4 cm	32 cm^2
10 cm	5 cm	50 cm^2

Its length is 10 cm and its width is 5 cm.

Alternative solution:

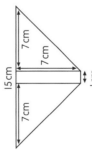

50 ÷ 2 = 25 cm^2
5 × 5 = 25 m^2
Width = 5 cm
Length = 2 × 5 = 10 cm

---

7 Miss Ali makes a path with a width of 1 m around her rectangular patch of land.
The length and width of the outer boundary of the path are shown in the shape.
Find the:
a perimeter
b area
of the rectangular patch of land.

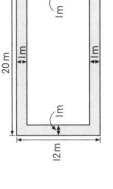

a Length = 20 − 1 − 1
= 18 m

Width = 12 − 1 − 1
= 10 m

Perimeter of patch of land = 18 + 18 + 10 + 10
= 56 m

b Area of patch of land = 18 × 10
= 180 m^2

8 A rectangular piece of paper 15 cm by 7 cm is folded along the dotted lines to make the shape shown.

Find the area of the shape made.

7 × 7 = 49
1 × 7 = 7

Area of shape = 49 + 7
= 56 cm^2

Problem Solving

1 Peter has a piece of cardboard as shown:

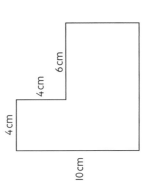

He wants to cut out as many squares as possible from the cardboard.
How many squares can he make if each side of a square is:

a 2 cm long?

b 3 cm long?

c 4 cm long?

a 19

b 7

c 3

---

3 A rectangular field has a length of 50 m and a width of 30 m.

a Find the perimeter of the field.

b Jack ran $\frac{3}{4}$ of the distance around the field. How many more metres must Jack run to go around the field once?

a 50 + 30 = 80

Perimeter = 80 × 2 = 160 m

b $\frac{3}{4}$ × 160 = 120

160 – 120 = 40

Jack must run 40 m more to go around the field once.

4 Miya's mum covers the floor of her living room, which measures 5 m by 6 m, with white and grey carpet as shown. Find the area of the floor covered with white carpet.

The area covered by white carpet makes a rectangle of length 6 – 0·5 = 5·5 m and width 5 m.

Area covered with white carpet = 5 × 5·5
= 27·5 m²

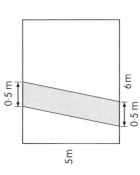

Date: _____

1 Find the number of seconds it takes for the second hand of a clock to move from:

a 12 to 7: __35__ s

b 3 to 11: __40__ s

c 6 to 2: __40__ s

d 9 to 5: __40__ s

2 Find the number of seconds it takes for the second hand of a clock to make:

a a half turn _____ 30 s

b one and three-quarter turns _____ 105 s

c two and a quarter turns _____ 135 s

d four complete turns _____ 240 s

3 Write the time using the 24-hour clock.

a 7:35 a.m. _____ 07:35

b 2:40 a.m. _____ 02:40

c 7:35 p.m. _____ 19:35

d 2:40 p.m. _____ 14:40

2 Figure A shows a piece of paper folded to make a square with sides of 8 cm as shown.
Figure B shows one of the flaps opened. Find the area of Figure B.

fold line

fold line

fold line

fold line

Figure A

8 cm

fold line

fold line

8 cm

Figure B

Area of Figure A = 8×8
= $64\,\text{cm}^2$

Area of one triangle = $64 \div 4$
= $16\,\text{cm}^2$

Area of Figure B = Area of 5 triangles
= 5×16
= $80\,\text{cm}^2$

3 This shape shows two squares. The area of the unshaded part of the shape is $9\,\text{cm}^2$. If the sides of both the squares are whole numbers, find the perimeter of the unshaded part.

1 cm

1 cm

4 cm

5 cm

	1st Guess	2nd Guess	3rd Guess	4th Guess
Area of big square	$2 \times 2 = 4$	$3 \times 3 = 9$	$4 \times 4 = 16$	$5 \times 5 = 25$
Area of small square	$1 \times 1 = 1$	$1 \times 1 = 1$	$2 \times 2 = 4$	$4 \times 4 = 16$
Area of unshaded part	3	8	12	9

From the 4th guess, side of big square = 5 cm
side of small square = 4 cm

Perimeter of the unshaded part = $5 + 5 + 1 + 4 + 4 + 1$
= $20\,\text{cm}$

Heuristic: Guess and check

Unit 12: Area and Perimeter

104

4

a A film started at 21:30. It was 90 mins long. What time did the film end?

21:30   22:30   23:00

The film ended at 23:00.

b A television programme began at 16:05 and ended at 17:30. How long was the programme? Give your answer in mins.

1h   25 mins

16:05   17:05   17:30

1h + 25 mins = 1h 25 mins
= 85 mins

The programme was 85 mins long.

c A television programme was 1h and 15 mins long. It ended at 00:35. What time did the television programme start?

15 mins   1h

23:20   23:35   00:35

The television programme started at 23:20.

5 A family drove from Cardiff to Edinburgh. After driving for $4\frac{1}{2}$ h, they stopped for 40 mins to have their lunch. They continued their journey for another 3 h and reached Edinburgh at 16:15. What time did they leave Cardiff?

30 mins   4h   40 mins   3h

08:05 08:35   12:35 13:15   16:15

They left Cardiff at 08:05.

6 The table below shows a selection of sports programmes on television.

Time	Programme
14:15	Football
16:30	Badminton
18:00	Cricket
20:15	Tennis
22:00	Rugby

a How long was the football programme?

1h   1h   15 mins

14:15   15:15   16:15 16:30

The football programme was 2h 15 mins long.

b Tom watched the badminton and tennis matches. How much time did he spend watching the two programmes?

1h   30 mins   1h   45 mins

16:30   17:30   18:00   20:15   21:15   22:00

1h 30 mins + 1h 45 mins = 2h 75 mins
= 3h 15 mins

Tom spent 3h 15 mins watching the badminton and tennis matches.

7 a The perimeter of a rectangle is 54 cm. Its length is 14 cm. Find its width.

14 cm

Perimeter = 54 cm   ?

54 ÷ 2 = 27
27 − 14 = 13
Its width is 13 cm.

b The area of a rectangle is 64 cm². Its width is 5 cm. Find its length.

Area = 64 cm²   5 cm

?

64 ÷ 5 = 12·8
Its length is 12·8 cm.

8 The shape below is made up of rectangles. Find its perimeter and area.

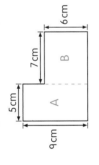

Perimeter
= 9 + 5 + (9 − 6) + 7 + 6 + 7 + 5
= 42 cm

Area of A = 9 × 5
= 45 cm²

Area of B = 7 × 6
= 42 cm²

Total area = 45 + 42
= 87 cm²

9 A rectangle is divided into 3 identical squares as shown. The area of the rectangle is 147 cm². Find its length and width.

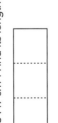

Area of each square   = 147 ÷ 3
= 49 cm²

Area of each square   = 7 × 7

Width of rectangle   = 7 cm

Length of rectangle   = 3 × 7
= 21 cm

10 A photograph measuring 12 cm by 9 cm is mounted on a rectangular piece of cardboard measuring 20 cm by 15 cm as shown.
Find:
a the area of the border.
b the perimeter of the border.

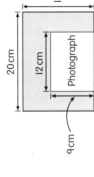

a   Area of cardboard   = 20 × 15
= 300 cm²

Area of photograph = 12 × 9
= 108 cm²

Area of border   = 300 − 108
= 192 cm²

b   Perimeter of border
= 20 + 15 + 20 + 15 + 9 + 9
= 88 cm

Unit 13: Symmetry

Medium-term plan

Week	Learning Objectives	Thinking Skills	Resources
2–3	**(1) Identifying symmetrical shapes** Pupils will be able to: • recognise symmetrical shapes • demonstrate whether a shape is symmetrical by folding paper	• Spatial visualisation • Comparing	• Pupil Textbook 4B, pp 117 to 122 • Practice Book 4B, pp 109 to 110 • Teacher's Guide 4B, pp 179 to 184
3	**(2) Identifying lines of symmetry** Pupils will be able to determine whether a straight line is a line of symmetry of a shape.	• Spatial visualisation • Comparing	• Pupil Textbook 4B, pp 123 to 126 • Practice Book 4B, pp 111 to 112 • Teacher's Guide 4B, pp 185 to 188
3	**(3) Making symmetrical shapes and patterns** Pupils will be able to: • cut out a symmetrical shape from a folded piece of paper • use a symmetrical shape to make a pattern • complete a symmetrical shape or pattern using a given line of symmetry *Let's Explore!* This task enables pupils to explore how symmetrical patterns can be created on square grid paper using a given line of symmetry.	• Comparing	• Pupil Textbook 4B, pp 127 to 132 • Practice Book 4B, pp 113 to 115 • Teacher's Guide 4B, pp 189 to 194
3	*Put On Your Thinking Caps!* These questions enable pupils to make use of the strategies of looking for patterns and acting it out to solve them.	• Spatial visualisation Heuristics for problem solving: • Look for a pattern • Act it out	• Pupil Textbook 4B, pp 133 to 134 • Practice Book 4B, pp 116 to 118 • Teacher's Guide 4B, pp 195 to 196

Symmetry

Learning objectives:
Identifying symmetrical shapes

Pupils will be able to:

- recognise symmetrical shapes
- demonstrate whether a shape is symmetrical by folding paper

Key concepts

- A symmetrical shape has a line of symmetry which divides the shape into two equal parts
- When folded along the line of symmetry, the two parts fit exactly

What you will need

Isosceles triangle (see Photocopy master 10 on p 245)

Unit 13 Symmetry

Let's Learn!

Identifying symmetrical shapes

1 These are symmetrical shapes.

The dotted line in each shape is a **line of symmetry**.

2 Fold shape A along the **line of symmetry**.

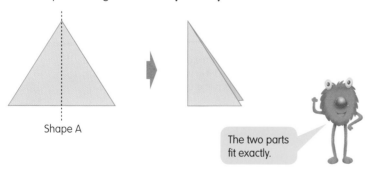

Shape A

The two parts fit exactly.

The shape is divided into equal halves by the **line of symmetry**.
The two equal halves fit exactly. So Shape A is a symmetrical shape.

117

Teaching sequence

1

- Ask pupils to refer to the two symmetrical shapes and their lines of symmetry in the textbook.
- Explain that each dotted line divides the shape into two equal parts. Demonstrate with a rectangular piece of paper that when it is folded along the dotted line, one half fits exactly over the other.
- We say that the rectangle is a symmetrical shape and the dotted line is called a line of symmetry.

2

- Repeat the demonstration with an isosceles triangle (Photocopy master 10). Emphasise the key point that for a shape to be symmetrical, it must have two halves that coincide exactly when folded along the line of symmetry.

What you will need

Right-angled triangle (see Photocopy master 10 on p 245)

Thinking skills

- Spatial visualisation
- Comparing

Note

Mirrors (preferably double sided) are a useful way for pupils to establish whether a given line is a line of symmetry. Mirrors are also used to find lines of symmetry in shapes.

Teaching sequence

- Demonstrate an example of a non-symmetrical shape by folding a right-angled triangle (Photocopy master 10) along the dotted line as shown in the textbook.
- Explain that as the two parts do not fit exactly, this right-angled triangle is not a symmetrical shape.

- Ask pupils to work on this question to informally assess their understanding of symmetrical shapes.

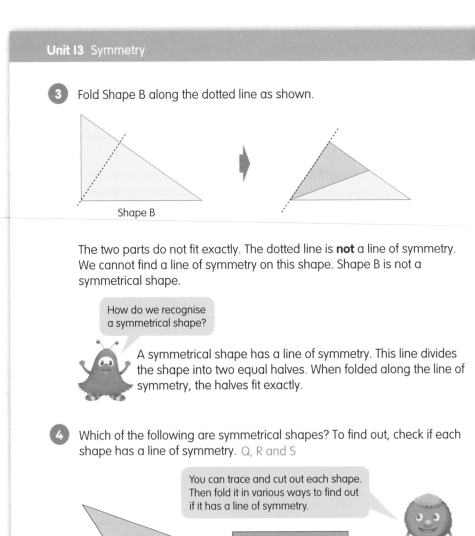

Unit 13 Symmetry

3 Fold Shape B along the dotted line as shown.

Shape B

The two parts do not fit exactly. The dotted line is **not** a line of symmetry. We cannot find a line of symmetry on this shape. Shape B is not a symmetrical shape.

How do we recognise a symmetrical shape?

A symmetrical shape has a line of symmetry. This line divides the shape into two equal halves. When folded along the line of symmetry, the halves fit exactly.

4 Which of the following are symmetrical shapes? To find out, check if each shape has a line of symmetry. Q, R and S

You can trace and cut out each shape. Then fold it in various ways to find out if it has a line of symmetry.

P   Q   R   S   T

118

5 The letters P and Q are not symmetrical shapes.

P ▶ P

Q ▶ Q

Why are these not symmetrical shapes?

6 Which of these are **not** symmetrical shapes?

A   B   C

Shape 1   Shape 2   Shape 3

D   F   J

Shape 4   Shape 5   Shape 6

Shapes [   ] are not symmetrical shapes. 2, 5 and 6

Home
Maths

Ask your child to trace and cut out the shapes in **6**.
Then fold the shapes along the dotted lines.
Ask them to show you which shapes are symmetrical and explain why.

119

Teaching sequence

- Show some examples of symmetrical and non-symmetrical letters of the alphabet, e.g. A, E, N, P and Q, with regard to given dotted lines.

- Ask pupils to identify the letters which are not symmetrical along the dotted lines.

Teaching sequence

- This activity enables pupils to apply their conceptual understanding of the line of symmetry to letters of the alphabet.

Activity

7 Use a pencil and paper or the drawing tool on a computer to write the letters of the alphabet from A to Z. Use capital letters.

Which letters are symmetrical? Record your answers in a table like this:

Letters Which Are Symmetrical	Letters Which Are Not Symmetrical
X	R

Compare your answers with your friends.

120

8 Which of these shapes are symmetrical? **a**, **b** and **d**

a

b

c

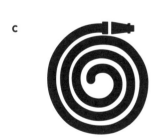

d

9 Which of the pictures below are symmetrical? basket, green vase and purple vase

Can you find more symmetrical shapes and objects around you?

121

Teaching sequence

8 and **9**

- Ask pupils to work on these questions for further practice on identifying the lines of symmetry in shapes and real objects.

Independent work

Practice 1 in Practice Book 4B,
pp 109 to 110.

Teaching sequence

10 and **11**

- Ask pupils to work on these questions to informally assess their understanding of symmetrical shapes.

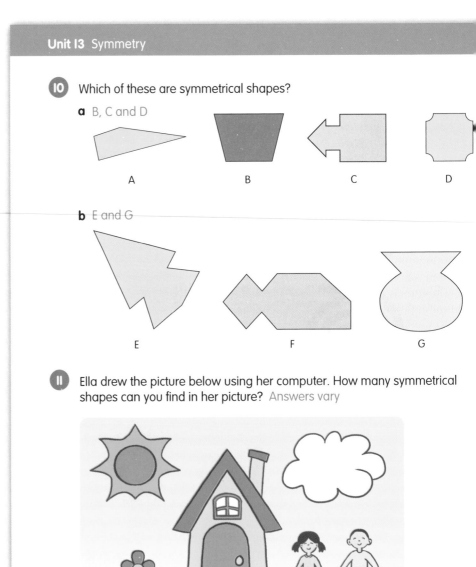

Unit 13 Symmetry

10 Which of these are symmetrical shapes?

a B, C and D

A   B   C   D

b E and G

E   F   G

11 Ella drew the picture below using her computer. How many symmetrical shapes can you find in her picture? Answers vary

Practice Book 4B, p.109

122

Learning objectives:
Identifying lines of symmetry

Pupils will be able to determine whether a straight line is a line of symmetry of a shape.

Key concept

A line of symmetry divides the shape into two equal parts so that the two parts fit exactly when the shape is folded along this line

What you will need

Pieces of rectangular paper

Thinking skills

- Spatial visualisation
- Comparing

Let's Learn!

Identifying lines of symmetry

1. Fold Shape A along the dotted line as shown.

Shape A

The two parts fit exactly. They are equal halves. The dotted line is a line of symmetry of Shape A.

2. Now fold Shape A along the dotted line as shown.

Shape A

The two parts fit exactly. They are equal halves. The dotted line is another line of symmetry of Shape A.

> A symmetrical shape can have more than one line of symmetry.

123

Teaching sequence

1 and **2**

- Demonstrate with a rectangular piece of paper, how a line of symmetry can be found by folding the rectangle along the dotted lines as shown in these examples.

- Discuss with pupils why the dotted lines in **1** and **2** are lines of symmetry on the rectangle.

- Encourage them to see that the rectangle is symmetrical about these lines because each line divides the rectangle into two equal parts which fit exactly when they are folded along the line.

- Explain to pupils that some shapes can have more than one line of symmetry and that a rectangle has two lines of symmetry.

Give each pupil a blank piece of
paper that is folded in half.

Ask pupils to open the paper,
drop paint onto the fold line and
then fold it back.

Ask pupils to draw on the line of
symmetry of the shape made.

Teaching sequence

3 and **4**

- Next fold the rectangle along
  the dotted lines as shown in
  the textbook.
- Discuss with pupils why these
  dotted lines are not lines of
  symmetry on the rectangle.
- Guide them to see that in **3**,
  the two halves do not fit
  exactly about the dotted line
  and in **4**, the two parts are
  not equal and therefore they
  do not match.

Unit 13 Symmetry

3 Look at the two halves made by the dotted line. Do the two halves fit
exactly? Is the dotted line a line of symmetry of Shape A?

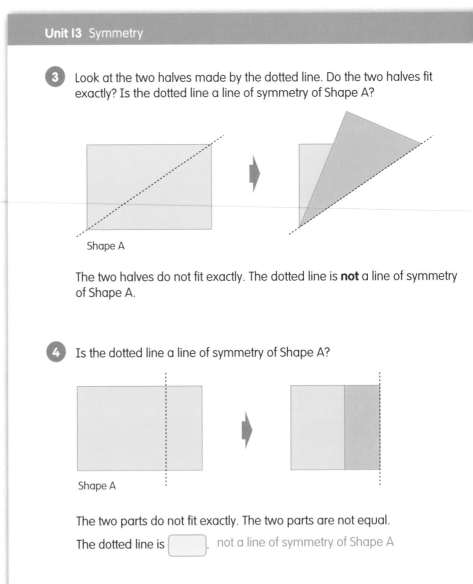

Shape A

The two halves do not fit exactly. The dotted line is **not** a line of symmetry
of Shape A.

4 Is the dotted line a line of symmetry of Shape A?

Shape A

The two parts do not fit exactly. The two parts are not equal.

The dotted line is [   ]. not a line of symmetry of Shape A

124

Additional activity

Ask pupils to work in groups of 3 or 4. Give each group cut-outs of a square, a rectangle and an equilateral triangle. Then ask the pupils to find the lines of symmetry of each shape.

5 Look at the following diagrams of Shape X. In each diagram, the dotted line divides Shape X into two equal parts. Trace the four diagrams of Shape X and cut them out.

Which of the dotted lines are lines of symmetry of Shape X?

Make sure you trace the dotted lines too.

A

B

Shape X

Fold Shape X along the line AB.

The two parts [fit] exactly.

Line AB is [   ]. a line of symmetry of Shape X

C ◄----------------► D

Shape X

Fold Shape X along the line CD.

The two parts [fit] exactly.

Line CD is [   ]. a line of symmetry of Shape X

F

E

Shape X

Fold Shape X along the line EF.

The two parts [   ] exactly. do not fit

Line EF is [   ]. not a line of symmetry of Shape X

G

H

Shape X

Fold Shape X along the line GH.

The two parts [fit] exactly.

Line GH is [   ]. a line of symmetry of Shape X

Teaching sequence

5

- Use this question to informally assess pupils' understanding of recognising lines of symmetry of a shape.

125

Teaching sequence

- To reinforce and consolidate pupils' understanding of lines of symmetry, ask them to carry out these activities.

Unit I3 Symmetry

Activity

6 **a** You will need a piece of paper containing the shape on the right.

   I Cut out the shape.

   2 Fold the shape to get:

     i two parts which are equal and fit exactly. Use a red coloured pencil to draw along the fold line.

     ii two parts which are equal but do **not** fit exactly. Use a blue coloured pencil to draw along the fold line.

     iii two parts which are **not** equal and do **not** fit exactly. Use a yellow coloured pencil to draw along the fold line.

Which of these lines is a line of symmetry? Why is the line a line of symmetry?

b Trace the shapes below and cut them out. Alternatively, you could use a computer to make the shapes.

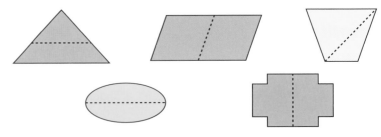

Draw a dotted line on each shape as shown above and fold along it. Which of the dotted lines are lines of symmetry?

Practice Book 4B, p.III

I26

Learning objectives:
Making symmetrical shapes and patterns

Pupils will be able to:

- cut out a symmetrical shape from a folded piece of paper
- use a symmetrical shape to make a pattern
- complete a symmetrical shape or pattern using a given line of symmetry

Key concept
A shape is symmetrical along a line if the line divides the shape into two equal parts and the parts fit exactly when the shape is folded along this line

What you will need
- Pieces of coloured paper
- Pieces of wrapping paper with patterns of symmetrical shapes
- Scissors

Thinking skill
Comparing

Teaching sequence

- Demonstrate how a symmetrical shape can be cut out from a folded piece of paper as shown in the textbook.

Symmetry **Unit 13**

Let's Learn!

Making symmetrical shapes and patterns

 a Jack folds a piece of paper in half. He cuts out a shape which starts and ends on the fold line like this:

Jack unfolds the shape. He gets a symmetrical shape like this:

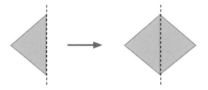

The fold line is a line of symmetry.

b Jack folds another piece of paper in half. Using the same method as before, he cuts out another symmetrical shape.

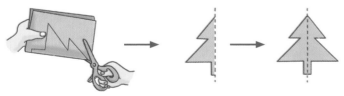

This fold line is also a line of symmetry.

127

Unit 13: Symmetry   189

What you will need

- Coloured paper
- Scissors
- Wrapping paper with patterns of symmetrical shapes

Teaching sequence

- Give each pupil a piece of coloured paper and a pair of scissors. Ask each pupil to cut out a symmetrical shape.
- Encourage pupils to show their shapes to the class and to explain why their shapes are symmetrical.

- Show pupils some pieces of wrapping paper which have patterns of symmetrical shapes on them. Ask pupils to identify the symmetrical shape used in each piece.

Unit 13 Symmetry

2. Fold a piece of paper in half. Cut out a shape which starts from a point on the fold line and ends on another point along the same fold line. Unfold your symmetrical shape. Compare your shape with those of your friends.

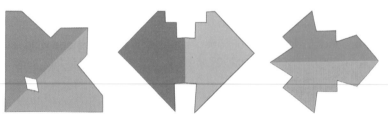

Here are some examples of symmetrical shapes.

3. Tai makes a wrapping paper pattern using this shape.

Can you find a line of symmetry in the shape?

Using this shape, he makes the pattern below on his paper.

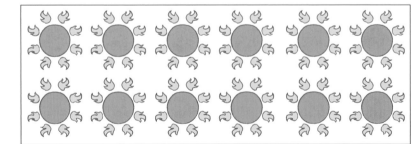

Visit an art gallery or clothes shop with your child. Look for pictures or clothes that have symmetrical shapes or patterns.
(1) Ask your child to draw a pattern that shows symmetrical shapes.
(2) Ask your child to draw a pattern that shows no symmetrical shapes.

128

What you will need

- Pieces of coloured paper
- Big sheets of paper
- Scissors

Activity

4 **a** You will need some coloured paper and a big sheet of paper.

    1 Fold a piece of coloured paper. Cut out a symmetrical shape.

    2 Make four copies of this shape.

    3 Stick the shapes on a big sheet of paper to make a pattern. Show your pattern to your teacher.

Example

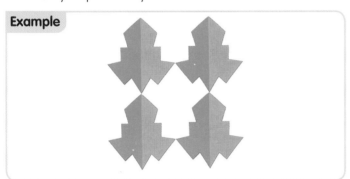

b Which of these designs are made up of symmetrical shapes? What are the symmetrical shapes used in these designs?

Answers vary

129

Teaching sequence

a

- This activity allows pupils to use their creativity to design patterns made up of symmetrical shapes.

b

- Ask pupils to answer this question for consolidation on identifying symmetrical shapes.

What you will need

- Square grid paper
- Scissors
- Ruler

Teaching sequence

5 to **7**

- These exercises require pupils to copy the shapes, patterns and the dotted lines onto square grid paper.

  Then they need to complete the symmetrical shapes and patterns by drawing the other half using the dotted lines as lines of symmetry.

- Ask pupils to cut out their shapes and fold them along the line of symmetry to check that they are symmetrical shapes.

5 Each shape below is half of a symmetrical shape. Copy them onto square grid paper. Then complete each symmetrical shape using the dotted line as a line of symmetry.

a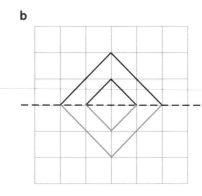

b

c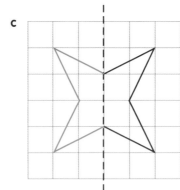

d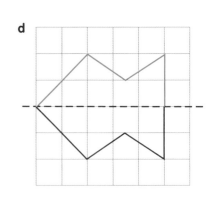

Independent work

Practice 3 and *Maths Journal* in
Practice Book 4B, pp 113 to 116.

6 Omar took two rectangular pieces of square grid paper as shown below.
He coloured some squares on one half of each piece of paper. Copy the
rectangles and colour the squares on the other half of each piece of paper
to make a symmetrical pattern.

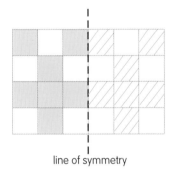

line of symmetry

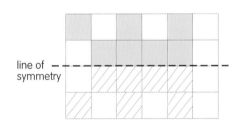

line of
symmetry

7 Each diagram below shows half of a symmetrical pattern. Copy these
patterns onto square grid paper. Then complete each symmetrical pattern
with the dotted line as a line of symmetry.

a

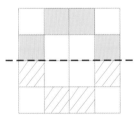

b

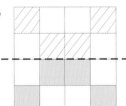

c

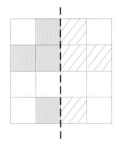

d

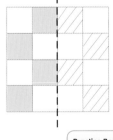

Practice Book 4B, p.113

131

Unit 13: Symmetry   193

Objective of activity

This task enables pupils to explore how symmetrical patterns can be created on square grid paper using a given line of symmetry.

What you will need

- Square grid paper
- Rulers
- Coloured pencils

Teaching sequence

8 *Let's Explore!*

- Pupils explore how symmetrical patterns can be drawn on square grid paper using a given line of symmetry. This enhances pupils' understanding of lines of symmetry.

Let's Explore!

8 You can create your own symmetrical pattern by using square grid paper and a coloured pencil.

1 Divide the square grid paper into halves by drawing a red dotted line as shown.

2 Colour a square on the left side of the square grid paper.

Left   Right

3 Colour a square on the right side of the square grid paper so that a symmetrical pattern is made.

Left   Right

4 Continue colouring the left side, and then the right side until you have designed your own symmetrical pattern.

Left   Right

132

Objective of activity

These questions enable pupils to make use of the strategies of looking for patterns and acting it out to solve them.

What you will need

- Square grid paper
- Ruler

Thinking skill

Spatial visualisation

Heuristics for problem solving

- Look for patterns
- Act it out

Teaching sequence

9 *Put On Your Thinking Caps!*

a

- Ask pupils to find out if there is a line of symmetry in each of the three patterns.

b

- Pupils have to find out how a non-symmetrical pattern can be made symmetrical by first visualising a line of symmetry, then identifying the square(s) to be shaded so as to make the pattern symmetrical along the line.

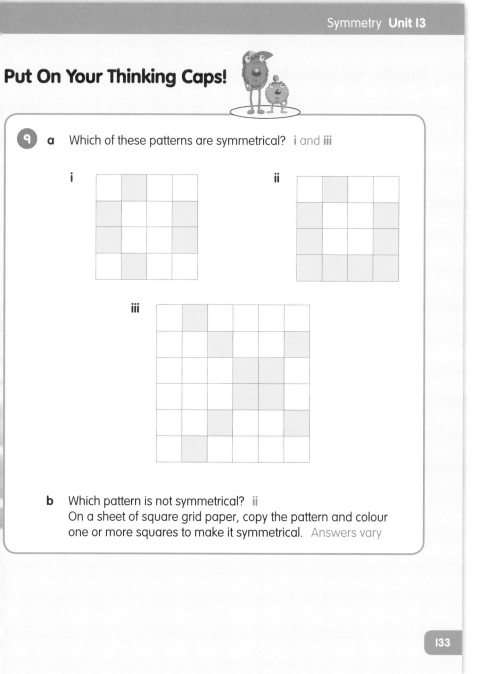

Put On Your Thinking Caps!

9 **a**   Which of these patterns are symmetrical? **i** and **iii**

i

ii

iii

b   Which pattern is not symmetrical? **ii**
On a sheet of square grid paper, copy the pattern and colour one or more squares to make it symmetrical. Answers vary

133

Independent work

Challenging Practice and
Problem Solving in Practice Book
4B, pp 117 to 118

Teaching sequence

10 *Put On Your Thinking Caps!*

- In this problem, pupils have to determine a line of symmetry and then identify where to add one unit square to each given pattern to make it symmetrical along this line.

11 *Put On Your Thinking Caps!*

- This problem is similar to **10** above. Here, pupils identify where to add three unit squares to each given pattern to make it symmetrical along the line of symmetry they have determined.

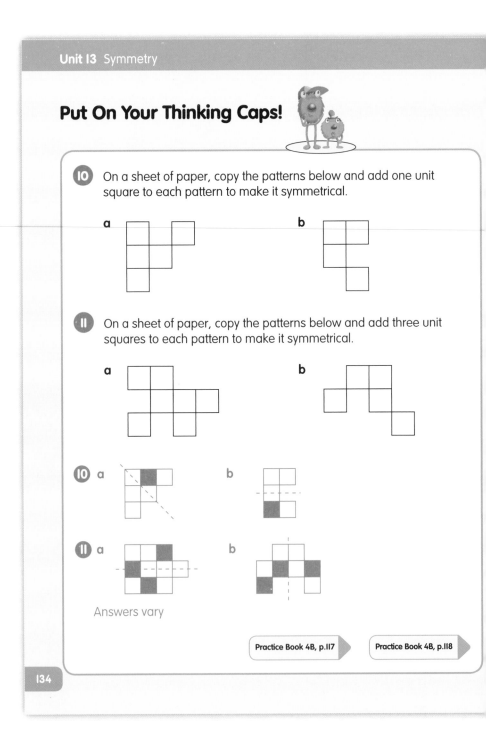

Unit 13 Symmetry

Put On Your Thinking Caps!

10 On a sheet of paper, copy the patterns below and add one unit square to each pattern to make it symmetrical.

a

b

11 On a sheet of paper, copy the patterns below and add three unit squares to each pattern to make it symmetrical.

a

b

10 a   b

11 a   b

Answers vary

Practice Book 4B, p.117

Practice Book 4B, p.118

134

Symmetry

Date: _____

Practice 1 **Identifying symmetrical shapes**

1 Some of the following are symmetrical shapes. Identify which shapes are symmetrical. Then fill in the space.

Shapes ___B, D, E, F, G, H___ are symmetrical.

Unit 13: Symmetry

109

Practice 2 Identifying lines of symmetry

1 Is the dotted line in each shape a line of symmetry? Write **Yes** or **No** in the spaces provided.

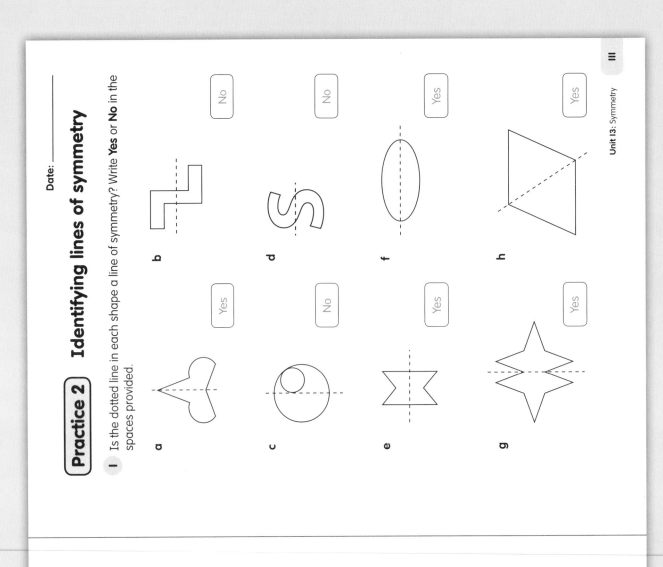

a Yes

b No

c No

d No

e Yes

f Yes

g Yes

h Yes

2 Which of these are symmetrical shapes?

a

b

c

d

e

f

Shapes _____ a, c, d, f _____ are symmetrical.

Practice 3

Making symmetrical shapes and patterns

1 Each shape is half of a symmetrical shape. Complete each symmetrical shape with the dotted line as a line of symmetry.

a
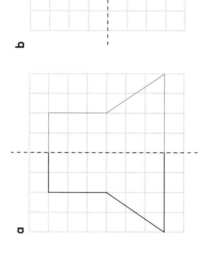

b

c

d
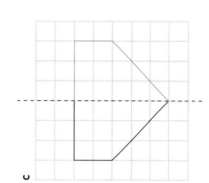

2 Is the dotted line in each number a line of symmetry? Write **Yes** or **No** in the spaces provided.

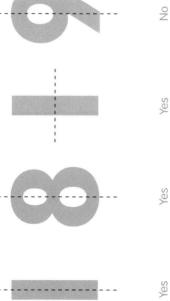

Yes   Yes   Yes   No

3 Make a symmetrical shape by folding a piece of paper in half and making a cut from one point on the fold line to another point on it.

Example

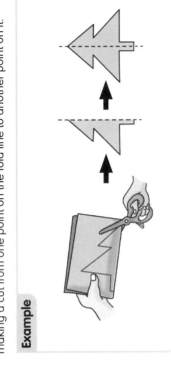

Make ten sets of your shape and create a design by making a pattern with the shapes. Draw or stick your pattern in the space below.

Answers vary

e

f

2 The dotted line on each pattern is a line of symmetry. Colour the correct squares or half-squares to make each a symmetrical pattern.

a

b

c

d

Challenging Practice

1 The dotted line is a line of symmetry.
Colour the correct squares or half-squares to make a symmetrical pattern.

a

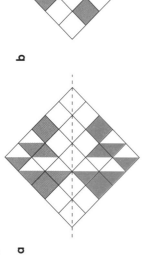

b

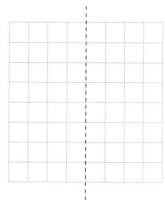

2 In the square grid below, design a symmetrical pattern with the dotted line as the line of symmetry. Answers vary

---

Maths Journal

1 Fill in the spaces using the words below.

| equal | halves | divides | line |

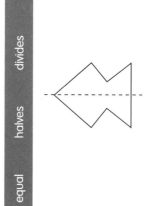

The dotted line is a line of symmetry of the shape because:

a it ___divides___ the shape into two ___equal___ parts.

b when the shape is folded along the ___line___, the ___halves___ fit exactly.

2

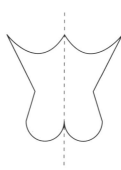

Explain why the dotted line is the line of symmetry for the shape.

a The line of symmetry divides the shape into two halves.

b When folded along the line of symmetry, the halves fit exactly.

Date: _____

Problem Solving

1   Peter is making a pattern of symmetrical shapes.
    He has made three of them.
    Can you help him to make the 4th one?
    Draw it in the space below.

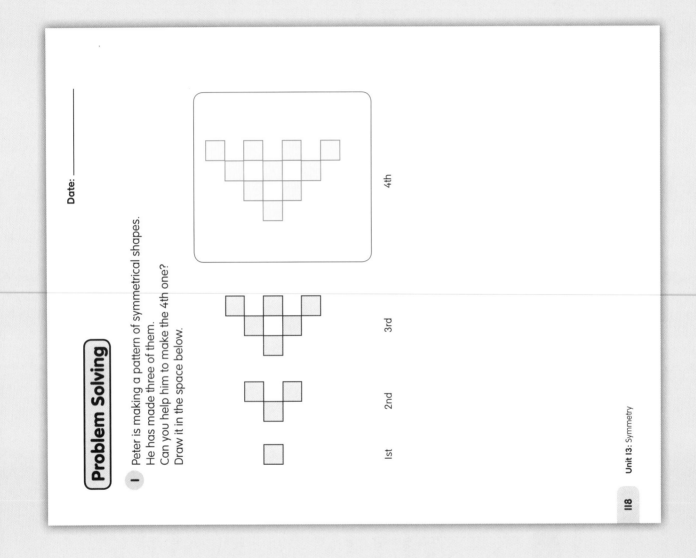

1st   2nd   3rd   4th

Unit 14: Tessellations

Medium-term plan

Week	Learning Objectives	Thinking Skills	Resources
4	**(1) Identifying tessellations** Pupils will be able to: • recognise a tessellation • identify the unit shape used in a tessellation • make a tessellation using a given shape *Let's Explore!* *Let's Explore!* enables pupils to find out whether all triangles can tessellate.	• Spatial visualisation	• Pupil Textbook 4B, pp 135 to 138 • Practice Book 4B, pp 119 to 122 • Teacher's Guide 4B, pp 205 to 208
4–5	**(2) More tessellations** Pupils will be able to: • tessellate a given unit shape in different ways • create a new tessellating shape from a given shape which tessellates	• Spatial visualisation	• Pupil Textbook 4B, pp 139 to 143 • Practice Book 4B, pp 123 to 126 • Teacher's Guide 4B, pp 209 to 213

Week	Learning Objectives	Thinking Skills	Resources
5	*Put On Your Thinking Caps!*	• Spatial visualisation	• Pupil Textbook 4B, p 144
	Put On Your Thinking Caps! enables pupils to discover that all four-sided shapes can tessellate.	Heuristic for problem solving: • Act it out	• Practice Book 4B, pp 127 to 130 • Teacher's Guide 4B, p 214
	Maths Journal		
	Maths Journal enables pupils to express whether they have mastered the concepts, skills and processes of this topic.		
	Review 7 Revision 2		• Practice Book 4B, pp 131 to 151

Summative assessment opportunities

Assessment Book 4, Test 6, pp 75 to 82
For extension, Assessment Book 4, Challenging Problems 4, pp 83 to 85
Assessment Book 4, Check-up 4, pp 87 to 98

Tessellations

Learning objectives:
Identifying tessellations

Pupils will be able to:

- recognise a tessellation
- identify the unit shape used in a tessellation
- make a tessellation using a given shape

Key concept

A shape can be tessellated if any number of them can be fitted together to cover a surface without any gaps or overlapping. If necessary, the shape can be rotated, but not flipped over.

Unit 14 Tessellations

Let's Learn!

Identifying tessellations

Look at the picture below. It shows part of a floor covered with rectangular tiles.

Look at these tiles.

Tiles of each shape can be used to cover a surface with no gaps between them.

 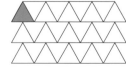 

These tiling patterns are called **tessellations**. Each tessellation is made with **one** shape. This is the **unit shape** of the tessellation.

135

Teaching sequence

- Show examples of tessellations, each made with a single shape called the unit shape.
- Emphasise that only the same unit shape is used in each tessellation. There are no gaps between the shapes and only one face of the shape is used (e.g. floor tiles where only one face of a tile can be used for tiling).
- Explain to pupils that a tessellating pattern continues forever.

Thinking skill

Spatial visualisation

Teaching sequence

- Show pupils examples of shapes that do not tessellate. Ask them to explain why these shapes do not make tessellations. Emphasise that they are not tessellations because there are gaps between the shapes or the shapes overlap.

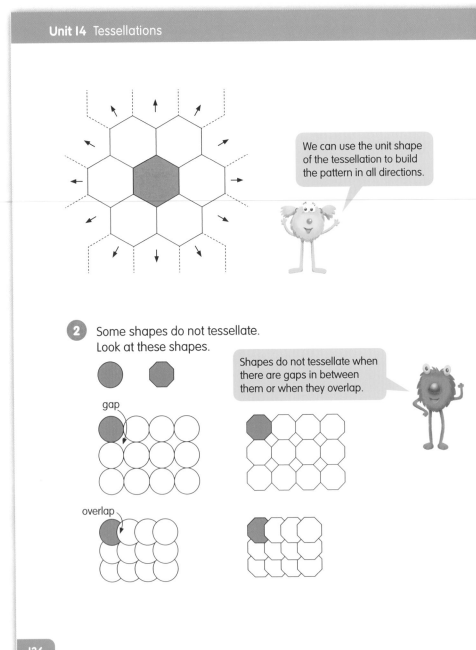

What you will need

- Unit shapes (see Photocopy master 12 on pp 247 to 248)
- Square dotty paper

3 Identify and draw the unit shape used in each of the following tessellations.

a

b

c

d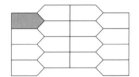

Activity

4 **a** Your teacher will give you ten copies of each of the following shapes. Find out which shapes tessellate. **1**, **2** and **3** tessellate.

1

2

3

b Copy each of the following shapes on a piece of square dotty paper. Make a tessellation with each shape. Answers vary

137

Teaching sequence

3

- Ask pupils to work on this question to informally assess their understanding.

4

a

- Give pupils ten of each of the three unit shapes (Photocopy master 12). They should use them to find out which of the unit shapes can tessellate.
- Pupils will discover that to make a tessellation, a shape may have to be rotated.

b

- In this activity, pupils are required to make a tessellation on square dotty paper. If necessary, give pupils a single unit shape to help them make the tessellation.

Objective of activity

Let's Explore! enables pupils to find out whether all triangles can tessellate.

Independent work

Practice I in Practice Book 4B, pp II9 to I22.

Teaching sequence

c

- Ask pupils to work on this question to informally assess their understanding of tessellations.

5 *Let's Explore!*

- Pupils work in pairs to explore whether all triangles can tessellate.
- Ask each pair to draw and tessellate a different triangular unit shape. Pupils should be able to conclude that any triangle can tessellate through this activity.

Activity

c   Draw and cut out the shapes below. Make ten copies of each shape and find out which shapes tessellate. **I** and **2**

1   2   3

Practice Book 4B, p.II9

Let's Explore!

5   Work in pairs.

I   Use a pencil, a ruler and paper or the drawing tool on a computer to draw a triangle and make twelve copies of it.

2   Cut the triangles out. Mark the angles as shown below and tessellate the triangles. Your triangle can be different from the one shown below.

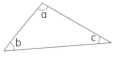

Can all triangles tessellate?

3   Show the tessellation of the triangle.

I38

Learning objectives:
More tessellations

Pupils will be able to:

- tessellate a given unit shape in different ways
- create a new tessellating shape from a given shape which tessellates

Key concepts

- A tessellating shape can cover a surface without any gaps
- Some tessellating shapes can cover a surface in more than one way
- A tessellating shape can be created from another

What you will need

Unit shapes (see Photocopy master 13 on pp 249 to 250)

Let's Learn!

More tessellations

1. Some shapes can tessellate in more than one way.
   For this shape , here are some ways it tessellates.

Answers vary

Draw another tessellation of this shape on a piece of paper.

Activity

2. Make ten copies of each shape shown below. Cut out each shape.
   Tessellate it in two different ways. Answers vary. Examples:

a

b

c

d

139

Teaching sequence

1

- Show pupils how some shapes, e.g. a square or an equilateral triangle can be tessellated in a number of different ways.

- Ask pupils to tessellate the given rectangle in another new way. Note that the length of this rectangle is twice its width.

2

- Ask pupils to cut out ten of each given shape (Photocopy master 13) and tessellate each shape in different ways.

Thinking skill
Spatial visualisation

Teaching sequence

- Ask pupils to draw and cut out ten of each given shape and tessellate each shape in different ways.

- Demonstrate how a new tessellating shape can be created from another unit shape.
- Start with a shape that tessellates, e.g. a rectangle. Cut out a piece (any shape) from one side of the rectangle and slide it to the opposite side. The resulting shape will also tessellate.

- If necessary, cut out another piece from a different side of the rectangle and slide it to the opposite side to get another tessellating shape.

Unit 14 Tessellations

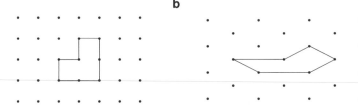

3 Draw and cut out the shapes below. Make ten copies of each shape and use them to make as many different tessellations as you can for each shape.

a   b

Answers vary

4 Millie designs a wallpaper pattern for an art competition. She shows how she designs the unit shape for her wallpaper from a square.

Millie's design:

Step 1   Step 2

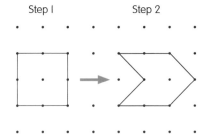 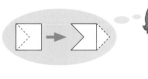

She cuts out the unit shape and makes copies of it. She colours half of the shapes blue and the other half of the shapes yellow. Then she tessellates the unit shape to make a wallpaper pattern.

Millie decides to improve her unit shape. She shows how she designs another unit shape for her wallpaper.

Millie's second design:

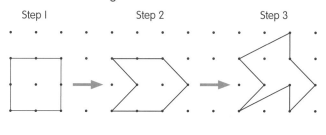

Step 1   Step 2   Step 3

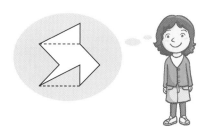

She cuts out this unit shape and makes copies of it. She colours the shapes. Then she tessellates the unit shape to make another wallpaper pattern.

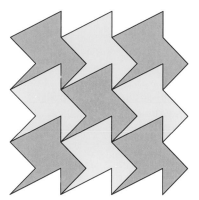

Teaching sequence

- Using a triangle, the piece that is cut out has to be rotated to make the new tessellating shape.

E.g.

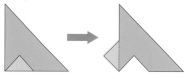

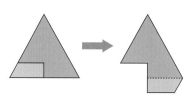

- If required, the cut-out piece can be translated and rotated to obtain the new tessellating shape.

E.g.

141

Hardeep shows how he designs the unit shape for his wallpaper pattern.

Hardeep's design:

Step 1   Step 2   Step 3

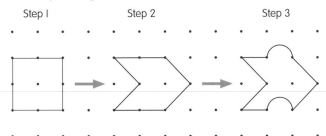

Hardeep also tessellates the unit shape to make his wallpaper pattern.

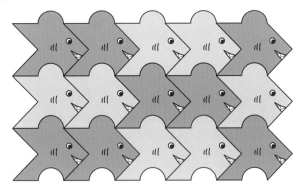

My wallpaper is made up of sharks!

Millie and Hardeep both designed unit shapes from a square. The square can tessellate, so the new unit shapes can also tessellate.

>
> **Home Maths**
> Encourage your child to try making some patterns that tessellate at home. Help your child to look out for unit shapes that tessellate in the world around them.

Independent work

Practice 2 in Practice Book 4B,
pp 123 to 126.

Activity

5 You will need some dotty paper. Design a unit shape that can
tessellate and make your own wallpaper pattern. Start with a shape
that can tessellate, such as one of the shapes below.

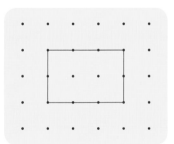
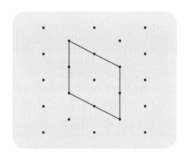

6 **Modify** each of the shapes below to design a new unit shape.
Make a tessellation for each new unit shape.

a

b

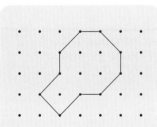
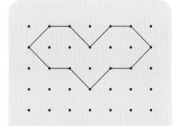

Answers vary

Practice Book 4B, p.123

143

5 and 6

- Pupils should use their
  creativity to design a new
  tessellating shape from each
  of the given shapes. Then they
  should make tessellations
  with the new shapes that they
  have created. If necessary,
  ask pupils to make copies
  of the shapes to make the
  tessellations as in 2 and
  3.

Objectives of activities

- *Put On Your Thinking Caps!* enables pupils to discover that all four-sided shapes can tessellate
- *Maths Journal* enables pupils to express whether they have mastered the concepts, skills and processes of this topic

Thinking skill

Spatial visualisation

Heuristic for problem solving

Act it out

Independent work

Challenging Practice, Review 7 and Revision 2 in Practice Book 4B, pp 127 to 151.

Teaching sequence

7 *Put On Your Thinking Caps!*

- Ask pupils to work in pairs to tessellate a four-sided shape.
- First they should draw a quadrilateral using a template. Then they draw the next quadrilateral by rotating it 180° about the mid-point of one of the sides. Pupils do this for the other three sides and repeat to continue the tessellation.
- Ask pupils to show their tessellations to the class and guide them to realise that any four-sided shape can be tessellated.

8 *Maths Journal*

- Pupils express their understanding of or difficulty with the concepts, skills and processes that they have learnt in this topic.

Put On Your Thinking Caps!

7 Work in pairs.

I Use a pencil, a ruler and paper or the drawing tool on a computer to draw any 4-sided shape and make twelve copies of it.

2 Cut out the shapes. Then mark the four angles as shown.

3 Make a tessellation with the shapes. Your 4-sided shape can be different from the one shown. Answers vary

> Practice Book 4B, p.127

Maths Journal

8 The list below shows what has been covered in this unit. Write down which parts of this unit you like the most and which parts you find difficult.

Tessellations:

a Recognise tessellations.

b Identify the unit shape of a tessellation.

c Recognise shapes that can tessellate.

d Draw a tessellation on dotty paper for a given shape.

e Draw different tessellations for a given shape.

f Design a unit shape and make tessellations with it.

144

Tessellations

Date: _____

Practice 1   Identifying tessellations

1 In each tessellation, colour the unit shape of the tile used.   Answers vary

a

b

c

d

3 Complete each of the following tessellations in the space provided by adding eight more unit shapes to each tessellation. Answers vary

a

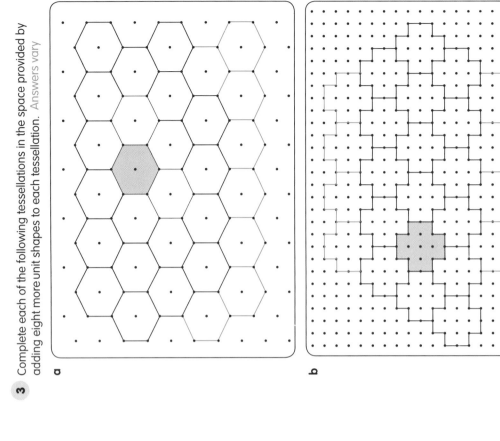

b

---

2 a Is each of the following tiling patterns a tessellation? Write **Yes** or **No** in the spaces.

i

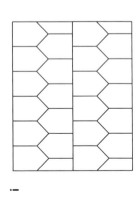

Yes

iii

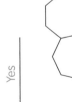

No

ii

Yes

iv

No

b Give reasons for your answers.

In **i** and **ii** the tiles of each shape fit with no gaps and can be extended in all directions, so these tiles can tessellate.

In **iii** the tiles overlap and in **iv** there are gaps between the tiles, so these tiles cannot tessellate.

Practice 2   More tessellations

1   Complete each of the following tessellations in the space provided by adding eight more unit shapes to each tessellation. Answers vary

a   Tessellation 1

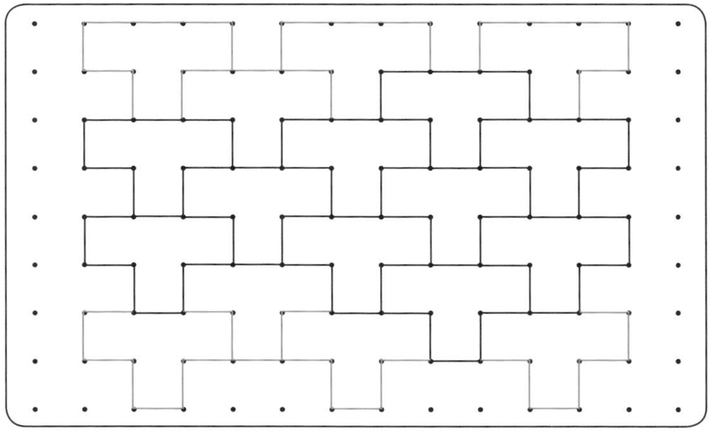

b   Tessellation 2

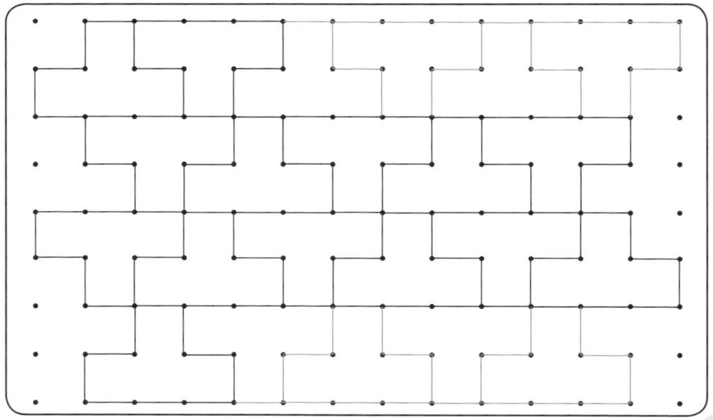

4   In each of the following, use the given shape to make a tessellation in the space provided. Answers vary

a

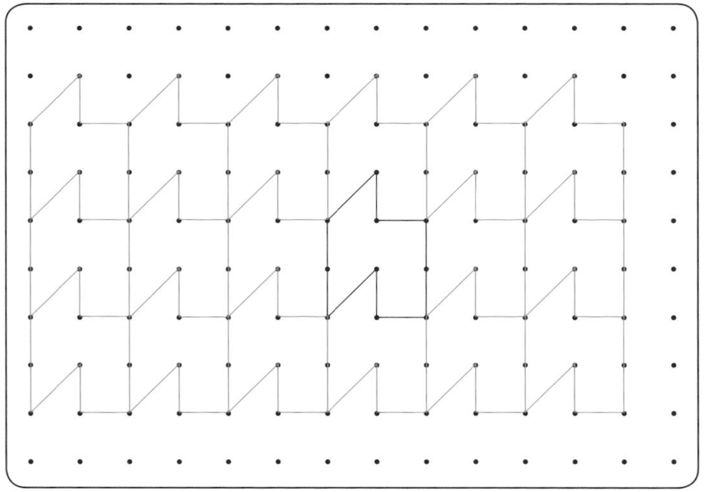

b

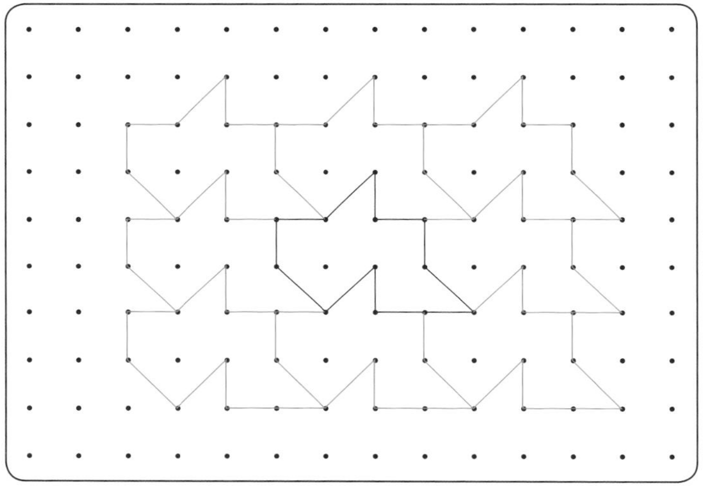

b   Tessellation 2

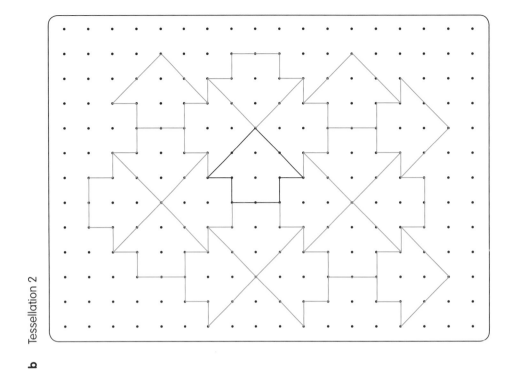

2   Use the given shape to make two different tessellations in the spaces
     provided. Answers vary

a   Tessellation 1

Date: _____

Challenging Practice

1 From the triangle below, create another shape which can also tessellate. Tessellate your shape in the grid provided below. Answers vary

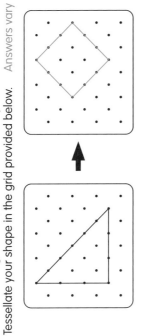

Shape A

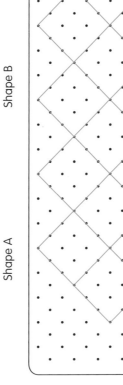

Shape B

---

3 From the square on the left, the shaded part is cut out and placed at the opposite side to make the shape on the right:

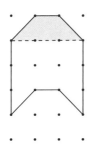

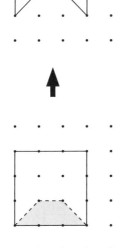

The new unit shape made is shown in the square dotty grid below. Use the shape to make a tessellation in the space provided. Answers vary

2

a From the square on the left, a semicircle is cut out to make the shape shown on the right.

Use the square dotty grid below to find out if this shape tessellates. Then fill in the space with **can** or **cannot**.

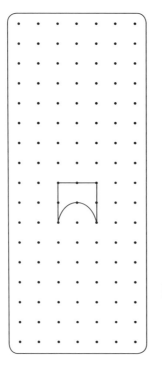

The shape ⊐ ___cannot___ tessellate.

b The shapes shown below are made by placing the semicircle that was cut out from the square in **a**:

on the opposite side to the cut-out side of the square

on the adjacent side to the cut-out side of the square

Use the grid below to find out if the shapes in **b** tessellate. Then fill in the spaces with **can** or **cannot**.

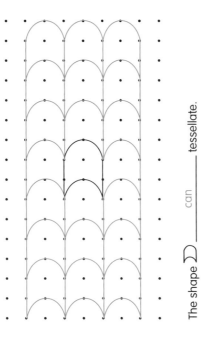

The shape ⊃ ___can___ tessellate.

The shape ⊃ ___can___ tessellate.

Review 7

1 A dotted line is drawn on each shape below. Is it a line of symmetry? Write **Yes** or **No** in the spaces.

a

No

b

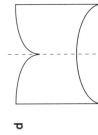

Yes

c

Yes

d

Yes

2 Is the dotted line on each shape below a line of symmetry? Write **Yes** or **No** in the boxes provided.

a

Yes

b

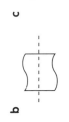

No

c

Yes

d

Yes

3 Use the shape below to make two different tessellations. Answers vary

a   Tessellation 1

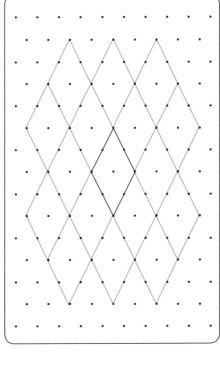

b   Tessellation 2

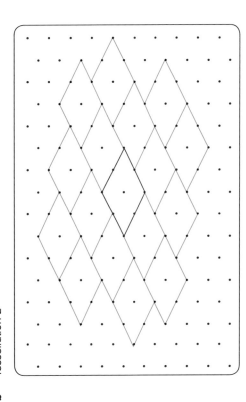

Answers Unit 14: Tessellations

221

3 Each shape below is half of a symmetrical shape. Complete each symmetrical shape with the dotted line as a line of symmetry.

a

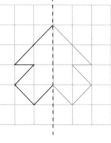

b

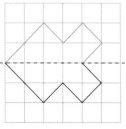

4 This shape is cut from a folded piece of paper. Complete the symmetrical shape that is made when the paper is unfolded.

Fold

5 In the shape below, is AB a line of symmetry? Explain your answer.

A - - - - - - - B

AB is not a line of symmetry because the two parts do not fit exactly.

6 Colour the unit shape used in each tessellation.

a

b

7 Complete the tessellation by adding 3 more unit shapes.

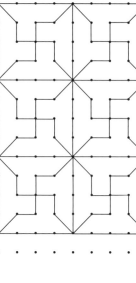

Revision 2

Section A

Choose the correct answer.
Write its letter in the box.

I 0·55 is not equal to _____.

a $\frac{11}{20}$　　　　b $\frac{55}{100}$ □

c $\frac{550}{1000}$　　　d $\frac{55}{10}$

2 The digit 9 in 89 412 stands for _____.

a 9 × 10　　　　b 9 × 100 □

c 9 × 1000　　　d 9 × 10 000

3 Round 36 985 to the nearest 100.

a 36 000　　　b 36 900 □

c 36 980　　　d 37 000

4 $4\frac{3}{5}$ = _____

a $\frac{12}{5}$　　　　b $\frac{20}{5}$ □

c $\frac{23}{5}$　　　d $\frac{43}{5}$

---

8 Use the given shape to make two different tessellations on the square dotty grids provided.

a Tessellation I

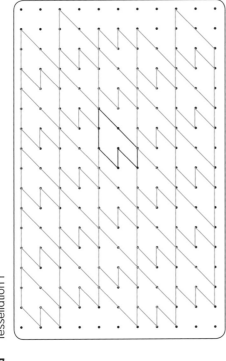

b Tessellation 2

5 The product of 9 and _____ is 1107.

a 123   b 1098

c 1116   d 9963

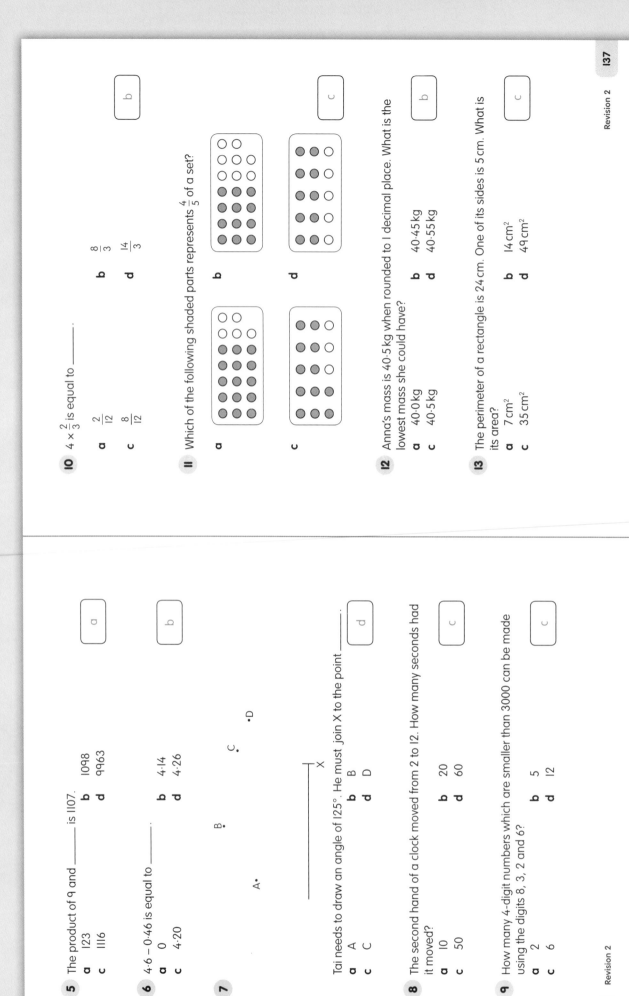

a

6 4·6 − 0·46 is equal to _____.

a 0   b 4·14

c 4·20   d 4·26

b

7

B.

A.   C.

•D

X

Tai needs to draw an angle of 125°. He must join X to the point _____.

a A   b B

c C   d D

d

8 The second hand of a clock moved from 2 to 12. How many seconds had it moved?

a 10   b 20

c 50   d 60

c

9 How many 4-digit numbers which are smaller than 3000 can be made using the digits 8, 3, 2 and 6?

a 2   b 5

c 6   d 12

c

10 $4 \times \frac{2}{3}$ is equal to _____.

a $\frac{2}{12}$ b $\frac{8}{3}$

c $\frac{8}{12}$ d $\frac{14}{3}$

b

11 Which of the following shaded parts represents $\frac{4}{5}$ of a set?

a   b

c   d

c

12 Anna's mass is 40·5 kg when rounded to 1 decimal place. What is the lowest mass she could have?

a 40·0 kg   b 40·45 kg

c 40·5 kg   d 40·55 kg

b

13 The perimeter of a rectangle is 24 cm. One of its sides is 5 cm. What is its area?

a 7 cm²   b 14 cm²

c 35 cm²   d 49 cm²

c

14 What is the shape of the tile used in the tessellation below?

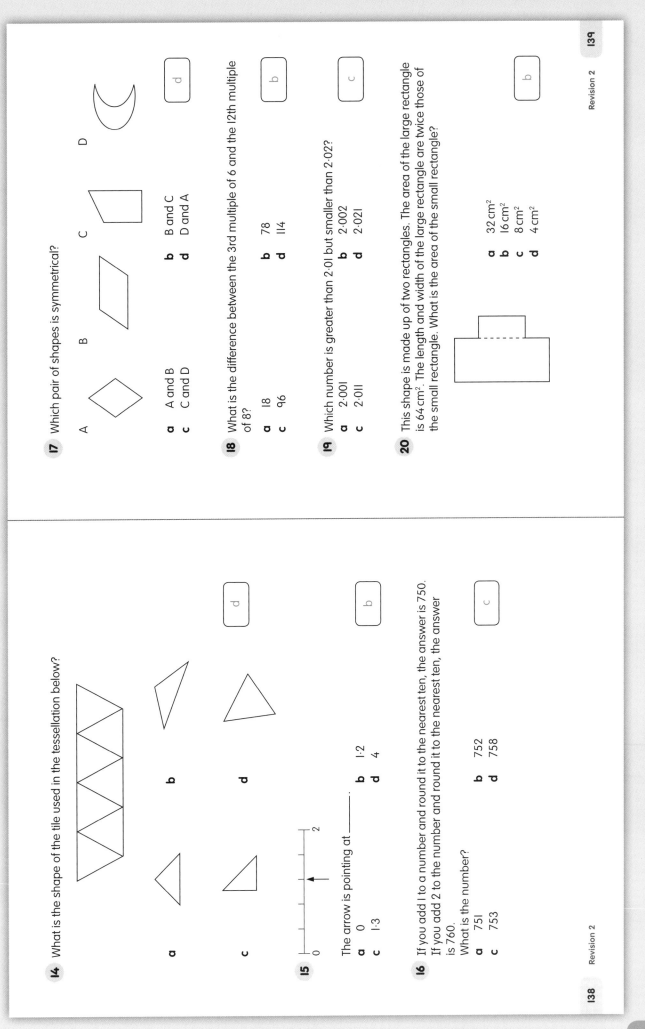

a b c d

d

15 The arrow is pointing at _____.

a 0
b 1·2
c 1·3
d 4

b

16 If you add 1 to a number and round it to the nearest ten, the answer is 750.
If you add 2 to the number and round it to the nearest ten, the answer is 760.
What is the number?

a 751
b 752
c 753
d 758

c

17 Which pair of shapes is symmetrical?

A B C D

a A and B
b B and C
c C and D
d D and A

d

18 What is the difference between the 3rd multiple of 6 and the 12th multiple of 8?

a 18
b 78
c 96
d 114

b

19 Which number is greater than 2·01 but smaller than 2·02?

a 2·001
b 2·002
c 2·011
d 2·021

c

20 This shape is made up of two rectangles. The area of the large rectangle is 64 cm². The length and width of the large rectangle are twice those of the small rectangle. What is the area of the small rectangle?

a 32 cm²
b 16 cm²
c 8 cm²
d 4 cm²

b

Section B

Read the questions and fill in the answers.

21 What is the missing value in the box?

$6.348 = 6 + 0.3 +$ ☐ $+ 0.008$

___0.04___

22 Omar spent $\frac{2}{5}$ of his money on a meal which cost £3·00. How much did he have left?

2 units → £3
1 unit → £3 ÷ 2 = £1·50
3 units → 3 × £1·50 = £4·50

___£4·50___

23 The table shows the number of marbles Jack and Miya have. Complete the table and answer the questions.

	Red Marbles	Blue Marbles	Total
Jack	18	26	44
Miya	37	24	61

a What is the total number of red marbles?

b What fraction of the total number of marbles is blue?

a Red marbles: 18 + 37 = 55
b Blue marbles: 26 + 24 = 50
Total number: 44 + 61 = 105

$\frac{50}{105} = \frac{10}{21}$

a ___55___

b ___$\frac{10}{21}$___

24 The line graph below shows the volume of drinking water in a water dispenser. Use the graph to answer the questions.

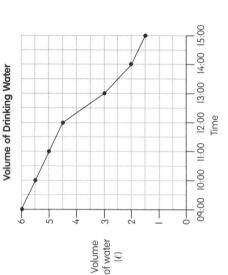

Volume of Drinking Water

Volume of water (ℓ) — Time

a How much water was there in the dispenser at 10:00?

b How much water was used between 12:00 and 13:00?

a ___5·5 ℓ___

b ___1·5 ℓ___

25 What is $\frac{2}{9} + \frac{2}{3} + \frac{4}{9}$?

$\frac{2}{9} + \frac{6}{9} + \frac{4}{9} = \frac{12}{9} = 1\frac{3}{9}$

$= 1\frac{1}{3}$

___$1\frac{1}{3}$___

26 Arrange the decimals in order. Begin with the smallest.
0·44, 0·404, 0·044

0·044, 0·404, 0·44

31 In the tessellation below, the unit shape is ⬭. Extend the tessellation in the space provided by adding 4 more unit shapes.

Answers vary

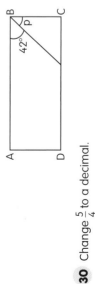

32 Farha's dad is 1·85 m tall. Round his height to the nearest tenth of a metre.

1·9 m

33 I am a number between 30 and 50. I am a multiple of 8. One of my factors is also a factor of 25. What number am I?

Possible numbers: 31, 32, 33, 34, 35, 36, 37, 38, 39, ㊵ 41, 42, 43, 44, 45, 46, 47, 48, 49

Multiples of 8: 8, 16, 24, 32, ㊵ 48, 56 . . .

Factors of 25: 1, 5 . . .

40

---

27 Rajesh planted some grass on a rectangular plot of land which measured 12 m by 8 m. He left a margin of $\frac{1}{2}$ m all around not covered by grass, as shown in the diagram below. Find the area of land covered by grass.

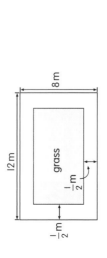

12 m

8 m

grass

$\frac{1}{2}$ m

$\frac{1}{2}$ m

77 m²

28

N

O

Ella is standing at the point O and is facing east.

a She turns through an angle of 135° in an anticlockwise direction. Which direction is she facing now?

north-west

b From the direction she is facing at **a**, she then makes a $\frac{1}{2}$ turn in a clockwise direction. Which direction is she facing now?

south-east

29 The shape below is not drawn to scale. ABCD is a rectangle. Find ∠p.

A

B

42°

p

D

C

48°

30 Change $\frac{5}{4}$ to a decimal.

1·25

37 How many grey squares must be replaced by white squares so that $\frac{2}{3}$ of the total number of squares are grey?

$$\frac{2}{3} = \frac{10}{15}$$

$$\frac{12}{15} - \frac{10}{15} = \frac{2}{15}$$

2

38 Multiply 0·87 by 8. Round your answer to one decimal place.

$0.87 \times 8 = 6.96$
≈ 7.0

7·0

39 Divide 3 by 8. Round your answer to 2 decimal places.

$3 \div 8 = 0.375$
≈ 0.38

0·38

40 Colour some squares and half-squares to make a symmetrical pattern in the diagram below.

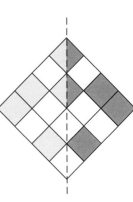

34 Draw a line parallel to CD passing through the point X.

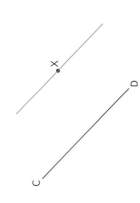

35 Draw a line perpendicular to AB passing through the point O.

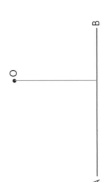

36 The length and the width of a rectangle are rounded to the nearest centimetre. The perimeter of the rectangle is 26 cm. Fill in the possible values of its length and width in the table below.

Perimeter of Rectangle = 26 cm

Length (cm)	12	11	10	9	8	7
Width (cm)	1	2	3	4	5	6

42 Complete the tessellation by adding 3 more unit shapes.

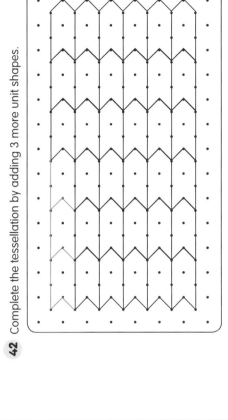

Section C

Read the questions.
Show your workings in the spaces provided.

43 Ella had some marbles. She gave $\frac{2}{5}$ of her marbles to Jack and $\frac{3}{10}$ to Farha. The rest of her marbles was given to Hardeep.
What fraction of the marbles did Hardeep get?

$\frac{2}{5} + \frac{3}{10} = \frac{4}{10} + \frac{3}{10}$

$= \frac{7}{10}$

$1 - \frac{7}{10} = \frac{3}{10}$

Hardeep got $\frac{3}{10}$ of the marbles.

41 Complete the tessellation by adding 3 more unit shapes.

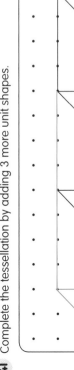

44 Peter had a roll of ribbon. He used 3·25 m of it to decorate some presents. This was $\frac{5}{6}$ of the roll. How many metres of ribbon did Peter have at first?

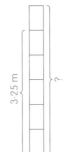

5 units → 3·25 m

1 unit → 3·25 ÷ 5 = 0·65 m

6 units → 6 × 0·65 m = 3·90 m

Peter had 3·90 m of ribbon at first.

45 Ella bought 2 books and 3 comics for £14·85 altogether. A book cost 3 times as much as a comic. Find the cost of 1 book.

2 books → 2 × 3 = 6 units

3 comics → 3 units

9 units → £14·85

1 unit → £14·85 ÷ 9 = £1·65

3 units → 3 × £1·65 = £4·95

The cost of 1 book was £4·95.

46 1 m of material cost £6·00. Ruby's mum bought 2·75 m of the material. She paid the sales assistant £50·00. How much change did she get?

2·75 × £6 = £16·50

£50 − £16·50 = £33·50

She got £33·50 change.

47 For a picnic Millie mixes 1·5 ℓ of squash with 7·75 ℓ of water. She pours the drink equally into 8 bottles. How many litres of drink are there in each bottle? Round your answer to 2 decimal places.

1·5 + 7·75 = 9·25

9·25 ÷ 8 ≈ 1·16

There are about 1·16 ℓ of drink in each bottle.

50 The area of a rectangle is 98 cm². Its length is twice its width. Find its length and width.

Using Guess and Check:

	1st Guess	2nd Guess	3rd Guess	4th Guess
Length	16	10	12	14
Width	8	5	6	7
Area	16 × 8 = 128 cm²	10 × 5 = 50 cm²	12 × 6 = 72 cm²	14 × 7 = 98 cm²

From the 4th guess, length of rectangle = 14 cm
width of rectangle = 7 cm

Its length and width are 14 cm and 7 cm respectively.

---

48 A chain has 175 links. The distance across each link is 4·95 cm. Estimate the total length of the chain in metres.

4·95 cm ≈ 5 cm
175 × 5 = 875 cm
= 8·75 m

The total length of the chain is about 8·75 m.

49 Mr Lee left his house and reached the supermarket at 14:50. He took 29 minutes to travel to the supermarket. He bought some food and left the supermarket at 15:30.
a What time did he leave his house?
b How long did he stay in the supermarket?

a

9mins   20mins
14:21   14:30   14:50

He left his house at 14:21.

b

10mins   30mins
14:50   15:00   15:30

He was in the supermarket for 40 minutes.

PHOTOCOPY MASTERS

Noogol

Googol

Koogol

Ooogol

Toogol

Zoogol

Unit 9: Decimals (I)

Let's Learn! (Pupil Textbook 4B, p 8)

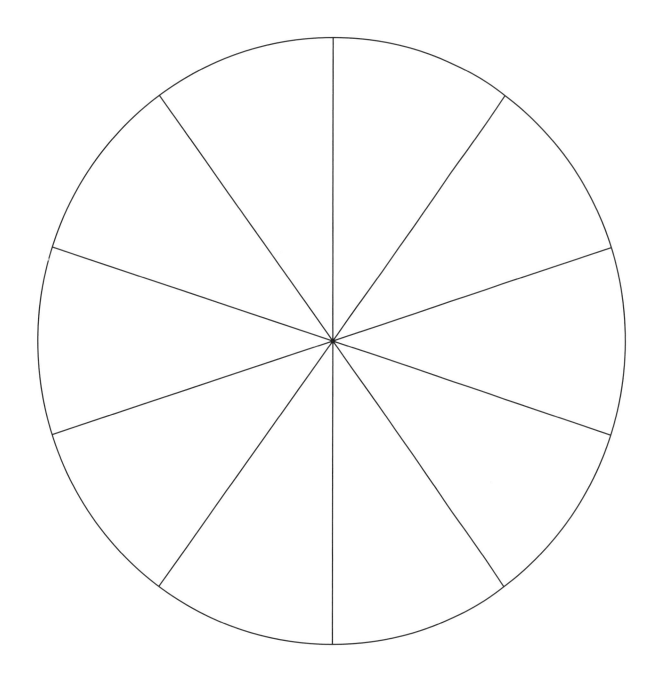

Unit 9: Decimals (I)

Unit 9: Decimals (I)

Let's Learn! (Pupil Textbook 4B, pp 8 to 9, 15, 22, 37)

Unit 9: Decimals (I)

Let's Learn! (Pupil Textbook 4B, pp 9 to 10, 48, 52 to 53, 62)

Ones	Tenths

Unit 9: Decimals (I)

Let's Learn! (Pupil Textbook 4B, p 14)

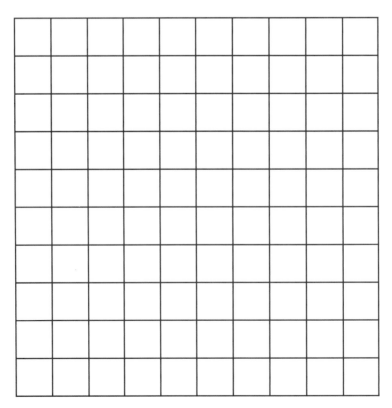

Unit 9: Decimals (I)

Let's Learn! (Pupil Textbook 4B, pp 15, 50, 63)

Ones	Tenths	Hundredths

Unit 9: Decimals (I)

Let's Learn! (Pupil Textbook 4B, p 21)

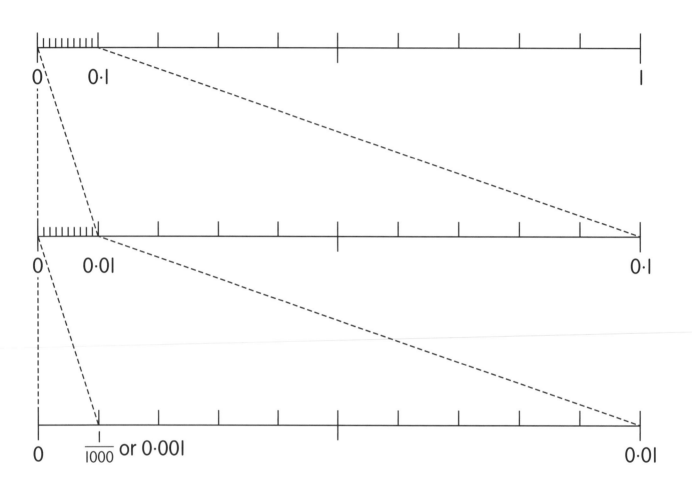

Unit 9: Decimals (I)

Let's Learn! (Pupil Textbook 4B, pp 22 to 24, 31)

Ones	Tenths	Hundredths	Thousandths

Unit 9: Decimals (I)

Game (Pupil Textbook 4B, p 44)

0.2	0.125	0.1
0.75	0.8	0.875
0.25	0.6	0.625
0.5	0.4	0.375

Unit 9: Decimals (1)

Game (Pupil Textbook 4B, p 44)

0.04	1.75	1.8
0.05	1.25	1.6
0.9	1.5	1.4
0.7	0.02	1.2
0.3		

Unit 9: Decimals (I)

Game (Pupil Textbook 4B, p 44)

$\dfrac{1}{2}$	$\dfrac{1}{4}$	$\dfrac{3}{4}$
$\dfrac{1}{5}$	$\dfrac{2}{5}$	$\dfrac{3}{5}$
$\dfrac{4}{5}$	$\dfrac{1}{8}$	$\dfrac{3}{8}$
$\dfrac{5}{8}$	$\dfrac{7}{8}$	$\dfrac{1}{10}$

Unit 9: Decimals (I)

Game (Pupil Textbook 4B, p 44)

$\dfrac{3}{10}$	$\dfrac{7}{10}$	$\dfrac{9}{10}$
$\dfrac{1}{20}$	$\dfrac{1}{25}$	$\dfrac{1}{50}$
$\dfrac{3}{2}$	$\dfrac{5}{4}$	$\dfrac{7}{4}$
$\dfrac{6}{5}$	$\dfrac{7}{5}$	$\dfrac{8}{5}$
$\dfrac{9}{5}$		

Unit 9: Decimals (I)

Put On Your Thinking Caps! (Pupil Textbook 4B, pp 46 to 47)

Unit 13: Symmetry

Let's Learn! (Pupil Textbook 4B, pp 117 to 118)

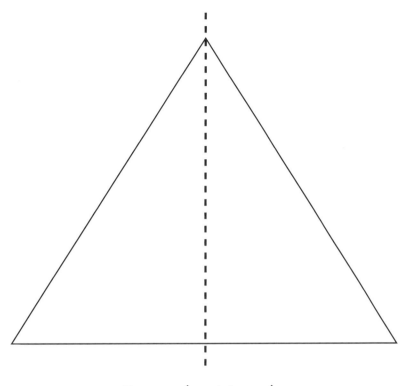

Isosceles triangle

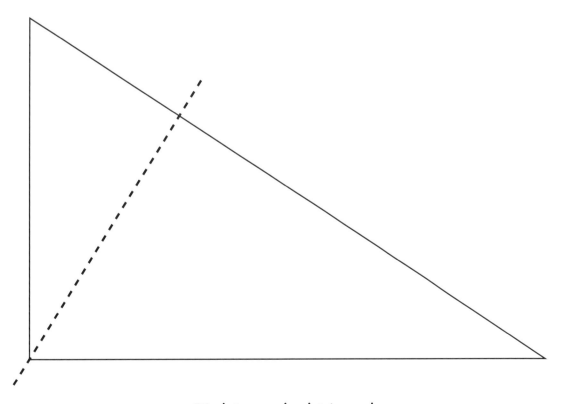

Right-angled triangle

Unit 13: Symmetry

Activity (Pupil Textbook 4B, p 126)

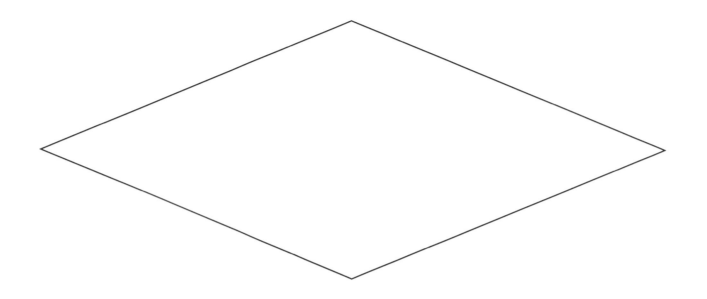

Unit 14: Tessellations

Let's Learn! (Pupil Textbook 4B, p 137)

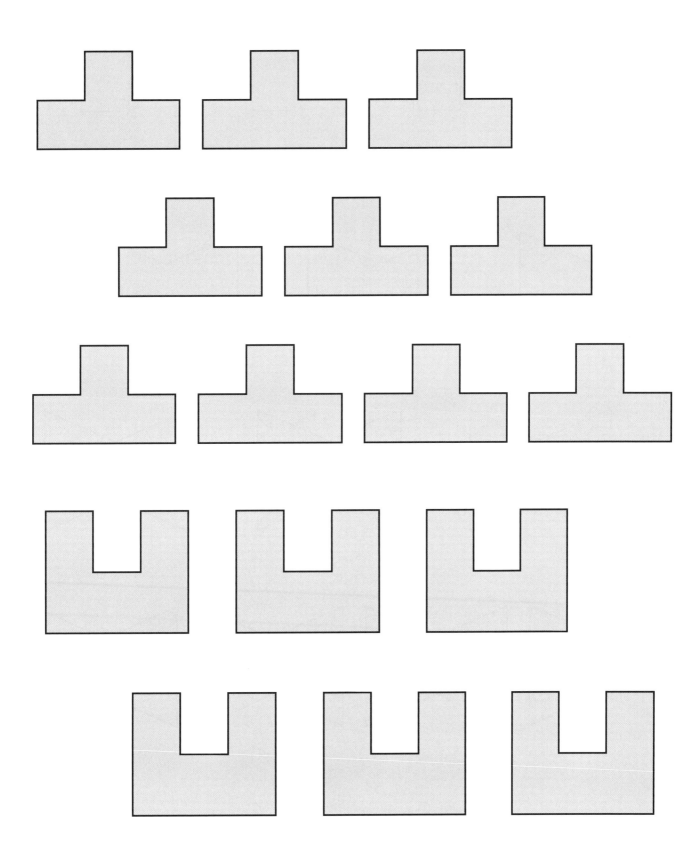

Unit 14: **Tessellations**

Let's Learn! (Pupil Textbook 4B, p 137)

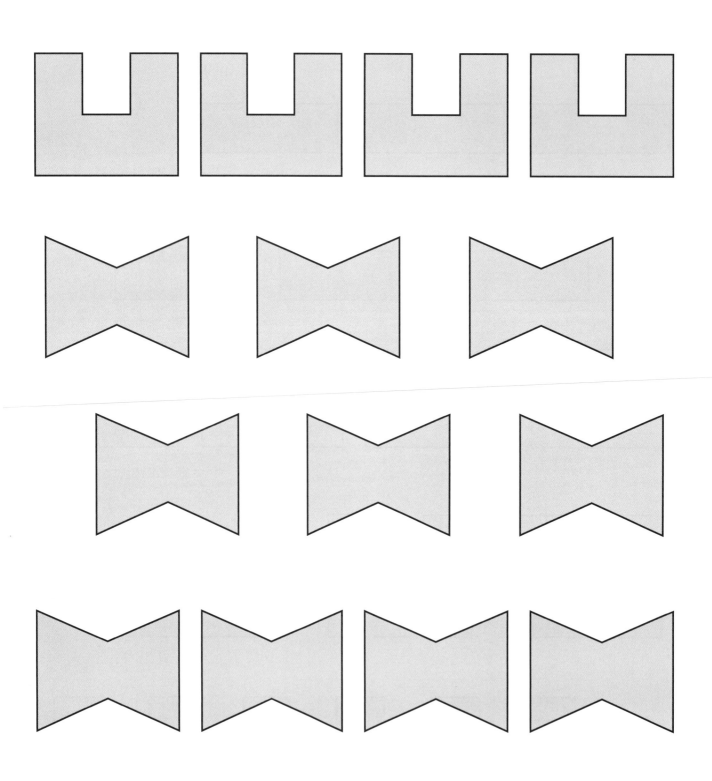

Unit 14: Tessellations

Let's Learn! (Pupil Textbook 4B, p 139)

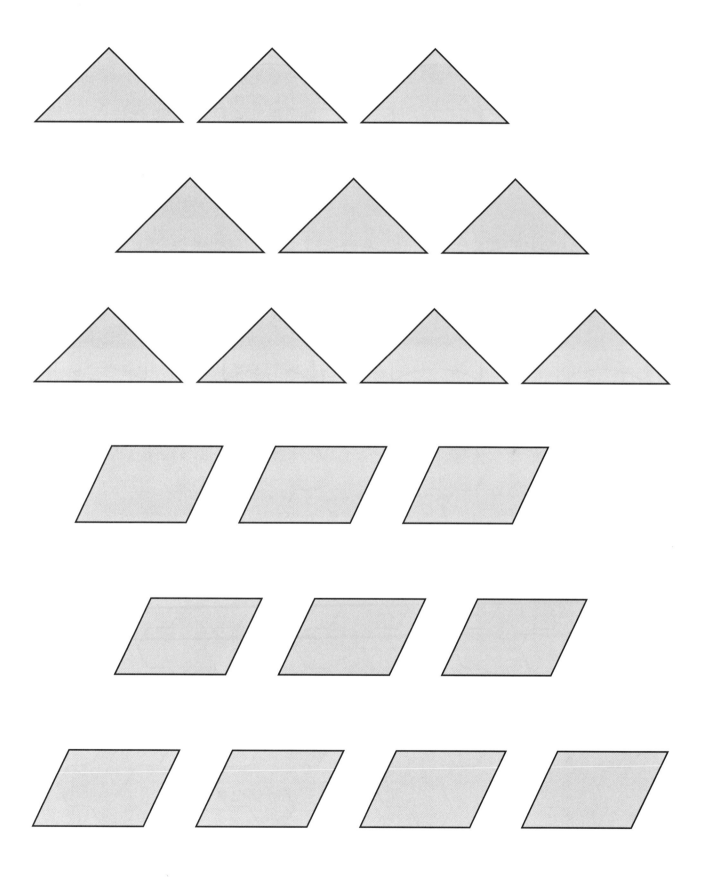

Unit 14: **Tessellations**

Let's Learn! (Pupil Textbook 4B, p 139)